Electronics for the Beginner

by
J. A. Stanley

Electronics for the Beginner

by

J. A. Stanley

HOWARD W. SAMS & CO., INC.
THE BOBBS-MERRILL CO., INC.
INDIANAPOLIS · KANSAS CITY · NEW YORK

SECOND EDITION

FIRST PRINTING—1968

Library of Congress Catalog Card Number: 68:9379

Contents

The Fun of Breaking

Into the Wonderful

World of Electronics

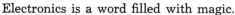

Electronics is a word filled with magic.

. . . To a scientist it is the *beep-beep-beep* from a satellite whirling in space.

. . . To the housewife, it stands for her new oven, which will broil a steak in five minutes.

. . . To the airline pilot, dropping a jet airliner onto a foggy airport runway, it could mean the difference between life and death for all persons aboard.

Electronics means *all* this, and much more. But to the writer, electronics is something else. Something mighty important in these days of high-pressure living.

Just Plain Fun

It is in the spirit of fun that this book is written. The book is filled with easy "how-to-do-it" plans for electronic equipment anyone—even with no previous electronic knowledge whatsoever —can build. The equipment is not only fun to build, but also to use.

For example, there is a crystal diode radio so simple that— even if you are all thumbs—you should be able to complete it in an hour or so, and know the thrill of building a radio that *works*.

There is a short-wave receiver which will pull in stations from halfway around the world. There is a unit which will enable you to go on the air and broadcast . . . a simple hi-fi . . . stereo . . . and many others.

Before doing anything else, skim through the book to become acquainted with it. Chances are you'll find several items you would like to build right now!

But wait a minute! Before tackling the Matterhorn, it is always wise to learn to wear shoes first. So let's look a bit closer at what is inside.

At first glance, the book may appear to be only a series of "do-it-yourself" building projects. It is true that the book *is* filled with plans for building many types of equipment. The plans proceed step by step, with drawings and photographs to illustrate how to connect *every* wire.

But there is a good reason for the building projects, in addition to the fun they can yield.

Why Roll Your Own

It is the writer's firm conviction—based upon nearly thirty years of matching wits with electronics gear—that the best starting point for learning about electronics is the actual building of equipment.

First of all, learning anything is more fun when you experience results as you go along, instead of simply reading about some rather abstract ideas. Likewise, once you *see* or *hear* something operate, understanding it becomes easier.

Moreover, in almost anything you do in electronics, some practical knowledge of building techniques is essential. For example, to do even the simplest servicing on a radio or TV set, you need some experience with tools and soldering, plus a hundred and one other techniques—ranging from how to strip the insulation off a wire, to how to apply heat to a crystal diode *without* ruining it.

This vital need for practical experience is the reason trade schools and the better electronics correspondence courses lean heavily on the building of equipment.

The same kind of practical experience is essential in the design of equipment (should you finally become a design engineer). There is a lot more to engineering than just circuitry. Take the matter of designing a set so it is easy to take apart for servicing. *Any* service technician will gladly name TV sets designed by men who evidently spent too much time at a drawing board and too little at a workbench. Simply getting some sets out of their cabinet is a task roughly akin to that of cracking a safe!

As you go on in electronics, you will want to assemble the many excellent kits available. From a kit you can produce equipment which looks and works like the manufactured product, but costs much less. However, before you build a unit you will want to keep, some experience is highly desirable. Also, you learn relatively little electronic "how and why" from assembling kits. The instructions are invariably slanted toward building of a single piece of equipment, with little explanation of the electronic background involved.

Building from plans initially, instead of from kits, has another advantage. If the sets have been carefully put together, you can use some of the same parts over and over again to build more complicated sets. Thus, you can have the fun—and experience—of building many *different* types of equipment without spending a fortune on parts.

Learn—The Easy Way

You will start out with such basics as learning how to use tools and how to put up an antenna. Then you'll progress through a series of building techniques, from the simplest "breadboard" layout, to a fairly complicated subassembly method. You will learn how to read electronic symbols . . . how to read circuit diagrams . . . how to identify and buy parts. Finally, you'll learn basic troubleshooting methods.

The learning will be as painless as we can make it. You will learn as a by-product of the other things you do. But learn you will. And if you have not yet decided upon a career, this book may open new doors for you.

As just one example, this book may kindle your interest in becoming a radio amateur—in the writer's opinion, the most satisfying hobby of all (and he has tried a lot of them). It is a valuable hobby, too, as many a young ham who has served in the Armed Forces has learned. If you have an amateur license as tangible evidence of your experience in electronics, the "welcome" mat will be rolled out for you. Chances are you will be immediately assigned to interesting electronic work, and will soon get one of those coveted stripes. Furthermore, "beetle crushing" (as the Air Force calls those long, long hikes) will be at a minimum!

Enough *about* electronics. Let's get our feet wet. Or more accurately, let's put our hands on some tools and parts!

CHAPTER 1

Tools and the Gentle Art of Soldering

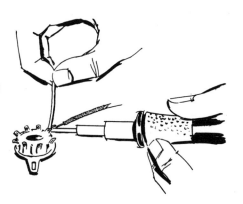

The thrill of taking a few electronic parts and putting them together to create a piece of equipment which comes alive with sound is one you will remember all your life. Like most good things, however, it has some pitfalls. One of these is the selection and use of tools needed to do the job. So the purpose of this chapter is to help you decide what tools to buy and how to use them.

Tools actually provide you with specialized "hands" for doing what would be impossible without them. For electronics work, literally hundreds of tools have been designed, many of them specialized types good for only one task. But, to get started, you will want tools which serve several purposes.

Tools for Holding and Bending

You probably already have some type of slip-joint pliers—the usual hand pliers which can be opened to handle fairly large objects. If you are buying a new pair, select one with a fairly thin "nose," because you often will be working in crowded quarters.

Always buy *good* quality tools because they *are* your hands for much of the building you will do. Poor quality tools make any job difficult. They may even make it impossible. Furthermore, tools—good ones—are virtually a lifetime investment. The writer is still using (after more than twenty years) several pliers he bought while in college.

Long-Nose Pliers

The slip-joint pliers mentioned are useful for such jobs as holding nuts and bending fairly large pieces of metal. However, for a lot of electronics work they are too big. The tool needed is a pair of long-nose pliers. The six-inch size will be large enough for most of your work; they need not have cutters. Long-nose pliers are highly useful, not only for slipping into places you can't reach with ordinary pliers, but also for form-

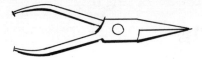

ing wire into loops. As an example, you can use them to loop the end of a light cord when you are attaching the cord to a plug or socket.

Tools for Turning

Of course you will need screwdrivers. Although good quality is advisable, the medium-priced ones will do the job well enough to get you started. Actually, you will need three sizes: one "pocket"

size, small enough to use on small setscrews in knobs; one medium size for ordinary machine and wood screws; and one fairly husky screwdriver. The third one won't see much use, but it will be a godsend when you tackle a "toughie," like removing a rusted bolt from some ancient radio you acquired for salvage.

The two pairs of pliers mentioned will take care of most of your needs. However, a pair of special socket wrenches—miniature versions of the cross wrenches used in removing wheel lugs to change a tire—will be extremely useful. Each tool has four sockets, giving a total choice of eight—just about 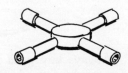 all you will ever need for working on most electronic equipment. These wrenches do a better job of turning or holding nuts than do pliers, yet are not nearly as expensive as a set of socket wrenches.

Tools for Cutting and Drilling

A crack TV service technician of my acquaintance says his most important service instrument is a pair of diagonal cutting pliers, which he uses to clip out bad parts. You won't be using them in this fashion for awhile, but you will use them constantly for snipping off ends of wires. They also make excellent wire strippers, and save buying an additional tool for this purpose.

The trick is to use your forefinger as a spacer to prevent cutting the wire while stripping off the insulation. Study the drawing, and then try out the technique on a length of insulated wire. It takes a little practice . . . you'll probably chop the wire in two the first time!

In buying diagonal cutting pliers, again buy quality. In fact, if you are buying only one quality tool, let it be the diagonal cutters. Since this tool is used for cutting, it will pay you to get the finest tool steel. This means the cutters will cost at least three dollars. A less expensive pair will soon nick along the cutting edges.

For sawing off shafts and cutting large holes in metal, you will need some type of hacksaw. Since the blades are usually of the same quality, regardless of the type of frame, a low-priced keyhole hacksaw costing less than fifty cents will do a satisfactory job.

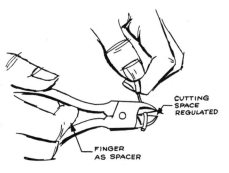

CUTTING SPACE REGULATED

FINGER AS SPACER

For drilling holes, a drill is a must. It may be either a hand drill or a power drill (if you can handle it). Buy the best one your budget allows. A set of drill bits, from $\frac{1}{16}$ to $\frac{1}{4}$ inch, is

BE SURE THE BITS WILL DRILL METAL!

ideal. However, just two drill bits, $\frac{5}{32}$ and $\frac{1}{4}$ inch, will handle a surprising amount of building. For larger holes, the drill you will need most often is the $\frac{1}{2}$-inch size. You can buy one with a shank that fits into an ordinary carpenter's brace.

Some type of pocket knife is needed, too. A good Scout knife is ideal because the *awl*, or *reamer*, blade is also highly useful.

Tools for Soldering

Yes, you will need a soldering iron. But note the word *iron*, not gun. The latter, although ideal for certain work, can get a beginner into real trouble. Unless used skillfully, it will become quite hot if not temperature controlled. The result can be over-

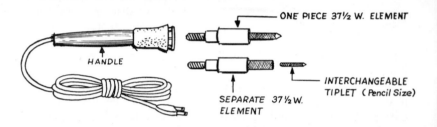

HANDLE

ONE PIECE 37½ W. ELEMENT

SEPARATE 37½ W. ELEMENT

INTERCHANGEABLE TIPLET (Pencil Size)

cooked solder joints or damaged small parts. For this reason, it is far better to start off with a soldering iron. Besides, the iron is less expensive.

An excellent iron to buy is one of the "pencil" types with interchangeable elements. This feature makes it possible for you to buy only one handle, and then screw in the different tips for handling light or medium work. For example, the handle can be fitted with a 37½-watt pyramid-tip element, which is adequate for fairly heavy work when the right solder is used. For light work or in tight quarters, the pyramid-tip element can be removed, and a 37½-watt element fitted with a pencil type "tiplet" used instead. This "tiplet," about the diameter of a lollipop stick, will enable you to work in mighty small spaces.

In addition to the iron, another tool, usually called a "soldering aid," will be a tremendous help. It is a piece of stainless-steel

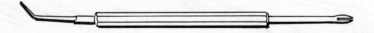

rod fitted with a wooden handle. One end of the rod is slotted, for gripping and twisting wire. The other end is pointed, for poking hot solder out of holes in lugs or other connectors. Because the rod is stainless steel, solder does not readily stick to it.

The Gentle Art of Soldering

Now, for soldering—the basic art in all electronic building. You *must* learn to solder and to solder *well*. More beginners have trouble with soldering than with any other phase of building.

Some new irons will need "tinning" before they are used. Because some irons are already tinned or require special treatment, be sure to follow the manufacturer's instructions. If none are given, do the following: File the tip of the iron until it shines. Then heat the iron, and coat the tip with solder. Tinning is the *only* time you apply solder *directly* to the soldering iron. More—a LOT more—on that subject later.

One of the best ways to learn any process is to study an actual example. So let's do exactly that. We'll start by soldering a wire to a tube socket—something you will be doing frequently.

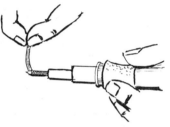

First, strip back the wire, using the "finger-in-the-diagonal" technique described earlier. But don't stop there. With a piece of sandpaper (or the blade of a knife), scrape the wire lightly until its surface is bright and as free as possible from oxidation (which might cause a bad solder joint). Do the same with the lug on the socket, even though it looks shiny.

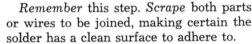

Remember this step. *Scrape* both parts or wires to be joined, making certain the solder has a clean surface to adhere to.

It is true, of course, that many parts you buy are already "tinned." Theoretically, with such parts you can skip the "scraping" step. However, until you have had considerable experience with soldering, the safest way is to scrape *everything*.

The next step is to join the parts mechanically so that all the solder has to do is make the electrical connection. Don't think of solder as a kind of glue—that isn't its purpose. Never, NEVER depend on solder alone to make the mechanical joint.

In our example of hooking a wire to a soldering lug, the wire should be fastened so securely to the lug that it will stay in place *before* any soldering is done.

To do this, first poke the wire through the hole in the tube-socket lug. Then tighten the wire to the lug by twisting it with the soldering aid mentioned. You may find it advisable to further "clamp" the wire with your long-nose pliers, to make the joint even more firm.

With the wire firmly fastened to the lug mechanically, we are now ready to begin soldering. But what kind of solder should we use? Here is what often constitutes a real pitfall for the beginner. The acid-core solder sold in hardware stores in worse than worthless. It is a downright menace, and can ruin your equipment. Actually, acid-core solder is intended for such metals as galvanized sheet metal. It is *not* suitable for wiring electronic equipment—*ever*. Instead, always use a noncorrosive solder designed for radio work.

Furthermore, to get good results easily, it is most important to use a particular type of radio solder, called 60/40. The figures mean that the solder is 60 parts tin and 40 parts lead. The greater quantity of tin results in a solder with a lower melting point than that of the fairly common 50/50 solder. The 50/50 solder is far more difficult for you—a beginner—to use. And under no circumstances should you even attempt to use 40/60 solder. Its high melting point often results in undesirable, "cold solder" joints, characterized by a pitted or grainy appearance. Solder for radio work contains an effective flux which chemically removes any small spots of oxidation you may have missed while scraping the parts.

In soldering, it helps a great deal if you start off with the right idea. For example, you do *not* heat the solder with the soldering iron!

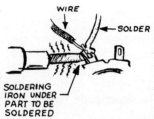

WIRE
← SOLDER
SOLDERING IRON UNDER PART TO BE SOLDERED

Read that last sentence again! It means exactly what it says. The proper method is to heat the *junction* (the area to be soldered) sufficiently so that the solder, when applied to the junction, quickly melts and flows onto it. Make sure the iron is hot before you start. Otherwise, the solder will pile up; and a cold-solder joint will result. Test the iron by applying solder to the tip. If it flows freely, the iron is hot. Before using the iron, wipe the melted solder off the tip with a rag.

There are two reasons for doing the job this way. First, for a good connection, all leads being joined together *must* be hot enough to melt the solder when it touches them. Second, heating the junction—instead of the solder directly—reduces the chance of burning up the flux before it has had time to do its work.

So, hold the iron underneath the joint to be made—*under-neath* because solder flows like water—down. *After* the joint has had enough time to heat up, apply the solder to the *top*. As the solder melts, it should flow down around the wire, and in and out of the lug hole, until there is a bright coating over the joint. Remove the iron from the joint, and allow the solder to harden.

Examine the joint carefully. It should look shiny and smooth—not pitted or grainy. If it has the latter appearance, reheat the joint, pry off the solder with the sharp end of the soldering aid, and start all over again.

If all looks well, give the joint time to cool. Then pull and tug on it to make certain the connection is firm. Should it break loose, count yourself lucky. You have discovered something which could cause you much trouble later. Make a new joint, and go through the same inspection again.

Like any other mechanical skill, soldering takes a little practice. But you will do all right if you will always follow these rules:

1. Use 60/40 noncorrosive radio-type solder—NEVER acid-core.

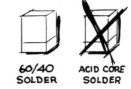

60/40 SOLDER   **ACID CORE SOLDER**

2. Scrape parts and wires clean and shiny before starting.

3. Make a good mechanical joint. Do *not* depend on the solder alone to make the mechanical bond.

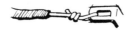

4. Make sure the iron is hot.

5. Heat the joint and flow the solder on.

6. Inspect the joint carefully. If in doubt, do it again.

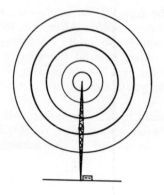

CHAPTER 2

Building a Trap

for Radio Waves

The fun of electronics really begins when you put together some kind of equipment which will unscramble radio waves so that you can hear them as voice or music. Doing this without some type of antenna requires a highly sensitive radio using half a dozen tubes or transistors. The latter will take a weak radio wave and multiply it *thousands* of times. So, the wave doesn't have to be very strong to start with; the feeble signal picked up by a "loop" within the set is good enough.

Sensitive equipment of this type is great—and some day you will want to build a few yourself, even though you may already own a couple of manufactured radios. But in getting started in electronics, you'll want to tackle simple equipment until you "get the hang of things." And simple equipment is not very sensitive.

Fortunately, you can make up for this lack of sensitivity by providing an antenna and ground. In this way you can increase the strength of the incoming signal so much that even an ultra-simple receiver (like the *One Hour* radio described in the following chapter) works very well indeed. Furthermore, an antenna is a necessity for short-wave reception, which you will probably want to work with eventually. You *must* have an antenna—should you decide later to become a ham operator—in order to broadcast to other ham operators, as well as tune in short-wave signals. So, before building any kind of electronic equipment, let's get started on the right foot by providing some kind of antenna.

Fortunately, erecting an antenna is a pretty easy task these days, thanks to the TV antenna manufacturers, who have worked out all sorts of brackets, masts, and insulators, etc. Cost will vary; depending on the shape of your lot, height of your house, etc. But chances are that you can put an antenna up for less than five dollars.

The Inverted L Antenna

There are innumerable types of antennas, but one of the best for the beginner is a simple **L**-shaped wire. As shown in the drawings, the end of the **L** is brought down into the house.

As mentioned, exactly how you lay out your antenna will depend on the available space. First, we'll assume you live in a house on a typical city lot. Later on, we will consider some ideas, should you live in an apartment building, or in some other spot where there are landlords or unsympathetic people to reckon with.

An ideal antenna is one made up of 90 feet of wire. Note from the drawing that this means 90 feet from the far end of

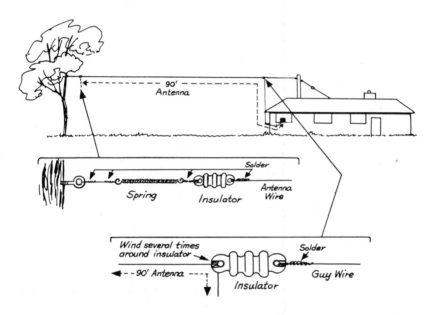

the insulator to the point where the antenna is hooked to your receiver. In a typical installation, the straightaway portion of the antenna might be 60 feet, with the remaining 30 feet used as the lead-in portion.

Yes, there is reason for the length of 90 feet. It happens to be an ideal length for a ⅜-wave Marconi transmitting antenna, should you decide later to become a short-wave ham broadcaster.

Notice that the drawing shows insulators at both ends of the antenna. Of course, there must be something on which to hook the insulators, to support the antenna high in the air.

Trees Are Quite Handy

If your house is fairly high and there is a convenient tree in the backyard, putting up the antenna is easy. All you need to do is provide some sort of short mast on the house, and then hook the insulator (on the far end of the antenna) to the tree. Of course, since trees move around in the wind, something is necessary to take up the slack. A screen-door spring will do the job very well (see the drawings). To fasten the spring to the tree, cut a piece of wire long enough to reach between the end of the antenna insulator and the tree. Hook this wire to a husky screw eye driven into the *trunk*—not a branch—of the tree. The screw eye will not hurt the tree, and this method is much neater than the more common practice of wrapping a wire around the tree. The latter method may damage the tree.

No trees? Then perhaps a mast erected on the garage will do. An ordinary two-by-four is strong enough for up to twelve feet or so, provided it is properly guyed. The guy wires can

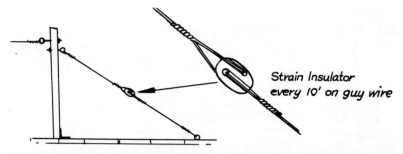

Strain Insulator
every 10' on guy wire

be galvanized wire of the type used to guy TV antennas. One or more strain insulators should be inserted at least every ten feet in the guy wire. The idea is to insure that no wire will be longer than ten feet — longer wires may upset reception slightly on short-wave bands. Strain insulators should be used because, if they should break, they will not open up the guy wire. The latter could be serious, depending on what is below when the antenna mast comes tumbling down!

Mounting the Mast

Erecting the two-by-four mast on the garage will, of course, depend on the type of roof, the shape of the garage, and so on. A common way to do the job is to bolt the mast to a strap hinge, and then secure the other half of the hinge to the roof with long wood screws. Make sure the screws bite into the roof rafters or other firm structure—shingles alone are not strong enough. This is important because quite a bit of pull is involved, more than enough to lift the shingles off the roof if a heavy wind comes along and they alone are supporting the mast.

Use of TV masts provide another, and perhaps easier, way to do the job, since you can select a suitable mounting bracket from the many ones available. An inexpensive variety (one suitable bracket costs about fifty cents) is adequate for the job if the TV mast is no taller than ten feet.

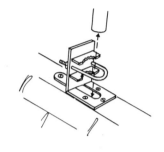

Just as with the strap hinge, make sure the mounting bracket is screwed to something solid.

The Wire Itself

Assuming we have worked out suitable supports for our antenna, the next step is to assemble the antenna itself. Obtain some No. 14 hard-drawn copper wire or (easier to handle) stranded bare copper wire. Size 7 × 24 stranded wire (7 strands, 24 gauge) is fine, and is one size commonly available for antennas. You will also need several TV standoff insulators (the number depends on how many bends you have to make and how far you run the lead-in portion of the antenna). Also buy a pair of antenna insulators — inexpensive glass or porcelain insulators are good enough.

Now measure off 90 feet of wire. Fasten one end of the wire to one of the insulators, by running it through the "eye" of the insulator a couple of times and then wrapping it tightly

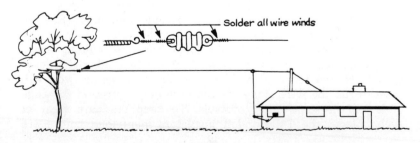

Solder all wire winds

onto the wire itself. Soldering the wire is a good idea—not to make a connection, but to insure that the joint with the insulator doesn't unravel. Run the wire to the insulator on the house. Wrap the wire through the "eye" several times, and then run it down the side of the house, leaving enough wire to go

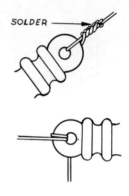

SOLDER

through the window (or other opening) and into the house. Note that the 90-foot over-all length is from the far insulator to the end of the wire in the house. How much of the wire is horizontal and how much is vertical doesn't matter—just as long as the over-all length is 90 feet.

Of course, if you simply haven't the space, you can put up a random length of shorter wire, even though it will not be as effective as the longer antenna. If you must reduce the over-all length, try to keep it at 45 feet—which happens to be the next shortest of the most desirable lengths.

How to Outwit Lightning

An antenna high in the air appears to be an open invitation to lightning. Actually, the chances of a direct hit are pretty remote at the usual height for most receiving antennas. But a lightning strike anywhere in the nearby area may induce a husky current in the antenna, perhaps even enough to cause damage. For this reason, outside antennas should be equipped with a lightning arrester. (Chances are there is one on your TV antenna.) To play safe, your antenna should also have an arrester. For lowest cost, it should be the type intended for single-wire lead-in. However, these are becoming hard to get, and a TV-type lightning arrester will work just as well. Actually, the TV antenna arrester is intended for a two-wire lead-in. But no matter—we simply use one of the lead-in terminals. Nothing is hooked to the other, as shown in the drawings. The ground connection is made to a ground rod or cold-water pipe. (See the instructions usually packed with the arrester.)

The antenna wire must be insulated from the building every foot of the way—from the insulator at the far end, right down to the antenna terminal on the receiver. Chances are you will have to run the wire alongside the building, or around the edge of a roof or some other obstacle. To keep the wire clear of such objects, the TV standoff insulators mentioned before are ideal. They come in various lengths, the 3½-inch size being very common. Screw them into the building wherever the wire must be kept clear of the building. They have a wood-screw type point which will go into wood or, in the case of a masonry house, into the mortar joints between the bricks.

Note that the insulators have a slot in one side to permit insertion of the flat TV lead-in wire. For our purpose, we want the slot closed. To do this, simply open the slip-joint pliers as wide as possible, and then squeeze down on the wire loop around the plastic insulator. This will close up the insulator, but still leave a hole through which we can thread our antenna wire.

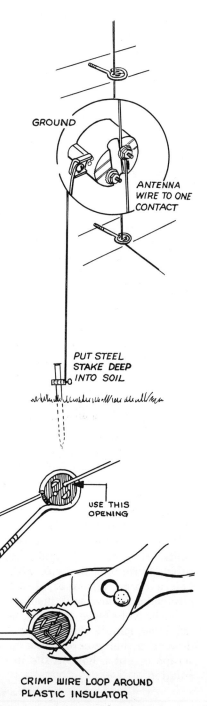

GROUND

ANTENNA WIRE TO ONE CONTACT

PUT STEEL STAKE DEEP INTO SOIL

Screw into Mortar

or

Wood

USE THIS OPENING

CRIMP WIRE LOOP AROUND PLASTIC INSULATOR

House Breaking Made Easy!

As you may have suspected, getting the wire into the house through a window or other opening can be quite a chore. The best way to do the job—if you really know your way around with tools, and have a broad-minded family or landlord—is to drill a hole right through the wall. For a masonry wall, the tool to use is a star drill—a special chisel which cuts out a tiny por-

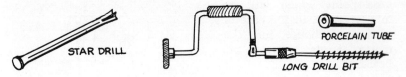

STAR DRILL

PORCELAIN TUBE

LONG DRILL BIT

tion of the hole with each blow from a hammer. In wooden walls (usually wood siding outside, plaster inside) a long drill bit of the type used by electricians will do the job easily. Another approach, if you have basement windows with wooden casings, is to drill through a casing, and then up through the floor, under the quarter-round trim. Once you have the hole through, you can slide in a tubular porcelain feed-through insulator—or, for better appearance (but higher cost), one of the TV-type through-the-wall insulators.

Somebody in your family takes a dim view of holes in the house? Don't despair, you have lots of company—and there are less drastic ways to do the job.

Perhaps the simplest way is to run the antenna wire between the window and the sill. Of course the wire must be insulated *from* the window. This is *particularly* important with the metal windows so common today.

One way to do this is to use a short length of the high voltage plastic tubing commonly used to protect the high voltage leads in TV sets. Any good TV shop should be willing to sell you a foot or so for a few cents. If you can't find the tubing, wrapping the wire with half a dozen layers of plastic electrician's tape will insulate it fairly well. Once the wire is insulated, simply close the window on it, being *careful* not to scrape or cut a hole in the insulation.

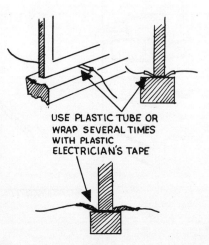

USE PLASTIC TUBE OR
WRAP SEVERAL TIMES
WITH PLASTIC
ELECTRICIAN'S TAPE

Look, Mom—No Connections!

Yes, there is even a way to get through a window which can't be opened. The answer is to make a kind of sandwich, with aluminum foil as the "bread" and the window glass as the "ham" in between.

To make this metal sandwich, bare the end of the antenna wire that comes down the side of the house to the window. Then take a one-by-two foot (or larger) piece of aluminum foil and

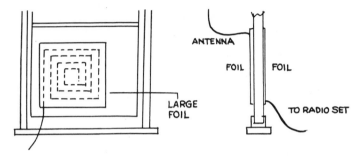

fold it over, being certain it makes good contact with the wire. (See drawings.) Cement the foil to the outside of the window with *Duco* china cement. (This type of connector can be purchased if you don't want to make one.)

Repeat the process inside, providing a lead-in wire which can be connected to the square aluminum sheet (double thickness) and to the antenna connection on the receiver. There is NO direct connection between the two pieces of foil—the glass is between them. What we have done is create a large *capacitor* (often called a *condenser*)—the pieces of foil on both sides form the *plates,* and the glass in between forms the *dielectric.* High-frequency radio waves will pass through such a capacitor without serious loss. The larger the pieces of foil, the less the loss.

For Apartment Dwellers Only

An outside antenna is the proper thing to use; the short-cuts which follow are intended *only* as a last resort. But if you live in an apartment or college dormitory, they may be the only way out.

One solution is to use an indoor antenna made up of the special flexible wire designed for such purposes. If you are on the second or third story of a building, the wire may do a passable job if strung along the outside edge of the floor. If you can sneak it down the hall, still better; every inch counts. The top edge of the ceiling of the room, particularly if it is of the older type with picture moldings, may be used. At any rate, get out all the wire you can—don't worry about the exact length.

Another solution is to "capacity couple" to the telephone line, and "hitchhike" on it as an antenna. One way to do this without disturbing the telephone is to wrap at least a foot of the flexible antenna wire around the telephone cord coming from

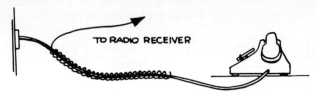

the wall. The result is a combination of inductive and capacitive coupling, but *no* direct connection to the telephone line.

How well this makeshift antenna works will depend on the amount of metal in the building, particularly in the conduit system (if any). However, it often works surprisingly well.

As a last resort, a direct (scraped) connection to bed springs may provide a modest antenna. Other possibilities include tapping onto an outside fire escape, downspout, or other metal on the outside of the house. Whether or not they will work can only be determined by experimenting with them.

Here is a final suggestion, if you have an understanding family and an *outside* TV antenna. The TV antenna itself isn't big enough for our purpose; but by hooking onto the lead-in line, we can use it for our antenna. One way to do this is to run a short wire from the receiver we are going to build, to an alligator clip. The latter is simply clipped to the antenna terminals on the TV set whenever we want the TV antenna to

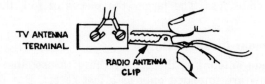

furnish signals to our small set. The TV set can remain connected at all times. But when you want a good picture on the TV set, you'll have to remove the clip!

In addition to an antenna, we need a ground. It can be an outdoor ground like the one mentioned previously, provided we can get a wire out to it. Or, start over again by running a wire (either bare or insulated) to a clamp on a *cold-water* pipe inside the house. Hot-water pipes are not as effective because the hot-water tank is between the connection and the cold pipe. Gas pipes are very poor because most of them are not grounded at all.

So, we have an antenna and ground hooked up, ready to be connected to our first radio. The antenna is fairly jumping with all sorts of radio signals. And it is surprising how little is needed to transform them into something we can hear. That is exactly what we will do next, by building the *One Hour* radio described in the following chapter.

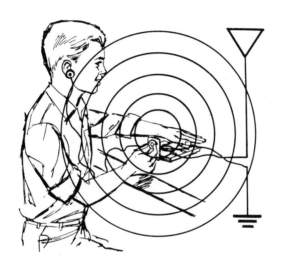

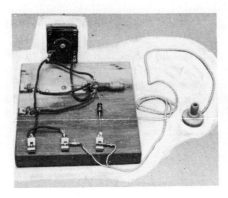

CHAPTER 3

The One Hour

Radio

Learning about electronics without *building* electronic equipment is like learning to swim without getting into the water. So let's dive in and build something!

Our first project is a radio with practically no parts at all. Yet it will tune in your strong *local* broadcasting stations in fine style. And late at night, with a good antenna like the 90-foot inverted **L** described in the previous chapter, don't be surprised if it pulls in stations up to 200 miles away (particularly after local stations go off the air, giving the weaker out-of-town stations a chance to be heard).

This receiver uses a kind of crystal detector called a *germanium diode*. This is a modern device which will handle far stronger radio signals than the old crystal did—and is also more sensitive. When combined with another modern part, a very

efficient high-Q coil, the result is a real radio capable of practical reception despite its simplicity. Because the parts are few, you can actually wire the set in less than an hour—hence the name, *One Hour* radio.

How It Works

Explaining in a few paragraphs how a radio works is quite a trick—many shelves of books have been written on the subject. But before wiring up our set, let's take a moment to consider what our little radio must do if we are to hear anything from it.

Sometimes the easiest way to understand anything complicated is to compare it with something familiar. In this case, we will look at the telephone.

First of all, we need to remember a basic fact about electricity. Electrical current is a flow of electrons, which behaves something like a flow of water. For example, if water is flowing in a garden hose and you step on the hose, the water flow will be *slowed down*.

Electric current works in exactly the same way as it moves along a wire. If we add *resistance* (just as we added *resistance* to the water flow when we stepped on the garden hose), we will *slow down* the flow of electrical current. (That is what a *resistor* does in a radio.)

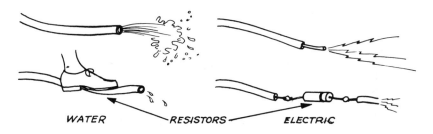

WATER   RESISTORS   ELECTRIC

Now—as you may already know—the microphone on a telephone is actually a kind of *variable* resistor which affects the flow of current on the telephone line.

When you speak into the microphone, sound waves produced by your voice strike a thin metal plate (diaphragm) inside the "mike." As the plate moves in and out, it alternately compresses and releases the pressure on the carbon particles inside the microphone. This changes the *resistance* these carbon particles

"MIKE"   RECEIVER

offer to the current. Thus, as you talk, you vary the amount of current flowing through the microphone and the telephone wire, which is connected to a receiver at the other end of the line.

The receiver you hold to your ear *responds* to variations in current—*exactly in step* with the words being spoken into the microphone. The diaphragm in the receiver goes in and out, also in step with the movement of the diaphragm in the microphone. As the receiver diaphragm moves, it re-creates the sound waves produced by the voice at the other end of the line.

So, with a telephone it is easy—because a *wire* connects everything together. But what about radio (or "wireless," as it was originally known)?

Remember that in our telephone we carried sound waves from one place to another by first causing the pressure of the sound waves to vary the current in the telephone wire. At the receiving end, we transformed this varying current back into sound waves.

The *wire* simply serves as the vehicle which carries our varying current. The current *variation* is the important item.

To the Moon and Back

If in some fashion we could use radio waves to carry the effect of our varying current, we would have a way to span continents—or for that matter, to carry a voice to the moon and back.

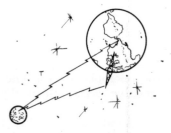

Of course, this is exactly what *does* happen in radio. We "hitch-hike" on radio waves sent out by a broadcasting station.

At the broadcasting station, we speak into a microphone and thus set up a varying current, exactly as we did on the telephone. In fact, you may have heard telephone conversations being broadcast over the radio.

By a process known as "modulation," the varying current from the microphone is combined with the radio wave in such

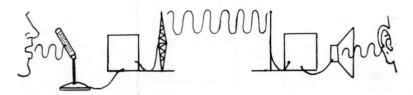

a way that the *amplitude* of the radio wave varies with that of the voice or other sound.

Our radio wave, complete with sound modulation, may travel to a radio set thousands of miles away. But, to get something we can hear, we must translate our incoming signal back into the form it had before it was combined with the radio wave.

Fortunately, this is easy to do. At the receiving end, we simply feed our modulated radio wave into one end of a germanium diode, the modern version of the crystal in the old-fashioned crystal set. From the opposite end of the diode comes the same kind of current we had on the telephone line. So, we have only to apply this varying current to a headphone or speaker, and we will hear sound.

Yes, it is possible to build a radio with only a diode, some kind of earphone, and an antenna and ground. Here is the hookup:

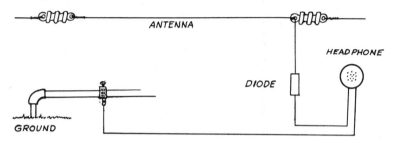

Such a radio will receive signals after a fashion, particularly if there is a strong station nearby. If there are two strong stations nearby, chances are you will receive *both* at the same time, which is pretty discouraging.

One important element is missing: some type of tuning device to enable us to choose the radio waves we want. The most common way of doing this is to use a coil and a variable capacitor. By properly combining these two parts, we can be more selective in our choice of stations—tuning in one, and tuning out others so that we hear them only very weakly, or not at all.

A simple radio, then, needs a tuning capacitor, coil, germanium diode, and an earphone. That is exactly what we use in the *One Hour* radio.

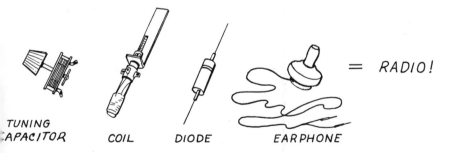

Let's Get To Building

To keep things simple, we'll use what old hands in radio call a breadboard layout. This means simply that everything is on top of a board—nothing is hidden underneath. For the set in the photographs, the board measures 5½ inches square. It may be a piece of one-inch pine, or any other soft wood such as Philippine mahogany or cedar. The board can be given a pleasing finish by sanding it and then rubbing with floor wax.

You will note in the picture that there is a small piece of hardboard (or quarter-inch plywood) supporting the variable capacitor. Follow the drawing in preparing this small panel. You can cut the hole needed ($\frac{5}{16}$") by first drilling it with your ¼-inch drill bit and then enlarging it slightly with a rat-tail file or small blade of a pocket knife, or the reamer blade of a Scout knife.

Shopping List—Cost Under $5.00

Now, let's collect the parts we need. Your local radio parts jobber should have them all. Here is what to ask for:

Quantity	Description	In Drawing, Part Labeled:
1	365-mmf (micromicrofarad) variable tuning capacitor. Single-gang miniature transistor type	A
1	Variable high-Q ferrite antenna coil. Coil should be the type to match the variable capacitor and have transistor tap.	
1	Germanium diode 1N34 or 1N34A	H / B
1	25-foot coil of push-back wire (solid No. 20)	
1	Package of soldering lugs	
5	Fahnestock or similar clips	C-G
9	Small wood screws	
1	Small knob	
1	Crystal earphone (or 2000 ohm magnetic)	

In building electronic equipment, the best practice is to mount as many pieces as possible *before* beginning the wiring. Note that the parts in the drawings are labeled with letters. Where there is more than one terminal on a part, each terminal also has a number. Thus, "A-1" is terminal number one on part "A"; "A-2" is the *second* terminal on the same part.

To help you keep track of each step as you do it, follow the instructions carefully, and then *check off* the step as it is completed. This helps avoid errors—the usual reason why something won't work.

☐ With wood screws, fasten a small hardboard mounting panel to the baseboard (see drawing).

☐ Remove the nut from the shaft of variable capacitor A. Insert the shaft through a hole drilled in the panel; then replace the nut, and tighten it down to secure the capacitor to the panel.

☐ Slide a knob onto the shaft of the capacitor. Secure it by tightening the set screw with a small screwdriver. (Or mount in whatever fashion knob requires—see drawings.)

☐ Along the outside of the board, mark the location for the five clips, following the drawing. With an ice pick or small nail, provide a starting hole for the wood screws.

☐ Run the wood screw through the hole in a clip, then through the hole in a soldering lug, and screw the clip to the board. With the slot on the end of your soldering aid, tip up the end of the lug so you can hook a wire to it easily. Repeat the process until all clips have been mounted.

☐ In most cases, you will find a small strip of metal mounting bracket packed with the coil. With your slip-joint pliers, bend one end of this metal strip at right angles so that the vertical portion is approximately ¾ inch high. This should be the portion containing the large mounting hole for the end of the coil.

☐ Secure this bracket to the baseboard with wood screws.

☐ The coil is fitted with a kind of snap-in end clip. Position the coil so the center lug of the three soldering lugs faces up. Then shove the metal end of the coil into the hole in the mounting bracket. Do this carefully, but firmly. Once you get the coil far enough into the bracket, small side clips will pop out and secure the coil to the bracket.

Now we're ready to start wiring. Any type of hookup wire will do, but push-back wire is by far the quickest and easiest to use. With this type of wire, you can simply cut it at the proper length by using your diagonal cutting pliers and then—by grasping the end of the wire between your thumb and forefinger—slide the insulation back far enough to give you the bare end needed for making a connection.

Heat up your soldering iron. If it looks dull and grimy, wipe the tip with a damp cloth until it shines. Do this frequently as you solder . . . an iron must be clean and bright to work properly.

In following instructions from this point on, note that two types of directions follow each step—those ending with the symbol "DS," and those ending in "S." "DS" means *connect* (by twisting, etc.), but do *not* solder—the reason being that other parts will be hooked to the same point later. "S," of course, means *solder*.

Important: The coil probably will have terminals arranged as shown in the drawings. However, not all brands are the same, even though they work equally well.

When you unpack the coil from its box, look at the enclosed diagram. It will indicate that the three connections to the coil are "ground," "tap," and "antenna." Make *certain,* in wiring the set, to use the ground connection for point B-1 in the wiring diagram. The tap should be B-2, and the antenna, B-3.

We Start Wiring

☐ Cut a wire of the proper length to reach from A-1 to B-1. Push back the fabric on the ends of the wire. Loop the bare wire through the lugs on A-1 and B-1, and crimp, using your soldering aid or long-nose pliers. Solder (S) the wire on coil terminal B-1. Do not solder (DS) the wire hooked to A-1.

☐ Run a second wire from A-1 (S) to lug E (DS).

☐ Connect lug E (S) to lug D (S).

☐ Connect lug G (S) to B-2 (S).

☐ Run the lead from lug F (S) to B-3 (DS).

☐ Run the lead from A-2 (S) to B-3 (DS).

☐ Loop the end of diode H into lug B-3 on the coil. Note that the "coding" line is *away* from the coil. Now, be *very careful.* First, get someone to help you. Have him grip the diode lead with the end of the long-nose pliers, between the coil lug and the diode (see drawing). Then solder all

TO COIL B-3   TO PHONE TERMINAL LUG C

DIODE CODING LINE

three connections to B-3. The reason for holding the pliers on the wire lead is to prevent excessive heat from reaching the diode and ruining it. The pliers will soak up the heat if handled as directed.

☐ Connect the other end of diode H to lug C. Again use pliers to absorb the heat (S).

Yes, that's all there is to the wiring! We're now ready to try out the set.

Hook the headphone to clips C and D. For best results, the headphone must be the crystal type. Fortunately, it is also the least expensive of the really sensitive earphones.

An excellent imported earphone of this type costs approximately a dollar and a half. If you want to test the sensitivity of your earphone before you buy it, touch the two tips to your tongue. If the earphone is sensitive, you should hear a weak click. This is caused by a battery action between the weak acids in your mouth and the metal of the phone tips.

Connect the antenna lug G (we are assuming you have a fairly good outside antenna). Connect the ground lead to clip E. (A *good* ground is just as important as a *good* antenna.)

Rotate the variable capacitor. Unless you have made a wiring mistake—or, and far more unlikely, have a defective part—as you turn the knob on the capacitor, you will tune in a local station.

Tune carefully—the little set has surprisingly sharp tuning, considering it has only one coil. (Many radios have six or eight.) Part of the secret is the high-Q coil. The fact that the antenna is fed to a tap, rather than to the end of the coil, also improves the selectivity.

If you have only a short antenna, or an indoor or make-shift one, connect it to the *short* antenna terminal. This will reduce the selectivity, but will increase the antenna coupling and thus give stronger signals on a small antenna. Even so, the results *won't compare* with those you get with a full-sized antenna.

You probably wonder what the threaded rod extending from the coil is for. It provides adjustment of the inductance (elec-

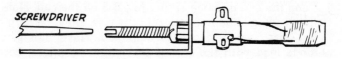

SCREWDRIVER

trical "size") of the coil. This is accomplished by moving a core in and out of the coil.

Chances are the coil was adjusted properly when it came from the factory. However, you may want to make some adjustment, particularly when you are using the short antenna terminal. Turning the screw so that it moves *out* lowers the inductance of the coil. This may be necessary if you have trouble tuning in stations at the "high" end of the dial on your regular home radio (toward the *16* or *1600* point).

If you want to fish for "DX"—which is what radio fans call trying to tune in distant stations—you will, of course, need a good antenna. You will also have to select a time when all—or at least most—local stations are off the air. For this kind of listening, you can hook the long antenna to the short-antenna terminal. Selectivity will be poor; but this won't matter much, since you won't be trying to tune out strong local stations, and you will need all the signal you can get.

Supposedly, 10 to 25 miles is about the limit for a diode-type radio. But the writer—and many others—have tuned in stations 500 miles away. And it is fun to do. Like tying into a big fish with a light line, there is something sporting about it!

You probably will do a lot of listening with your *One Hour* radio . . . there is something a bit uncanny about a couple of radio parts pulling music out of the air. Sooner or later, however you will want to take the next step—to make your set louder. In the next chapter we will do just that, using a transistor to amplify the signal from the *One Hour* radio.

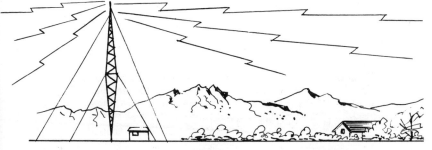

"Hints and Kinks"

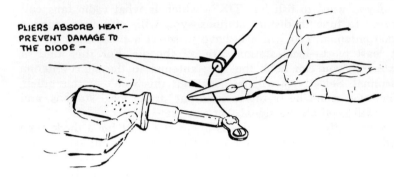

PLIERS ABSORB HEAT—
PREVENT DAMAGE TO
THE DIODE —

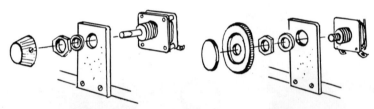

DIFFERENT CAPACITOR MOUNTINGS

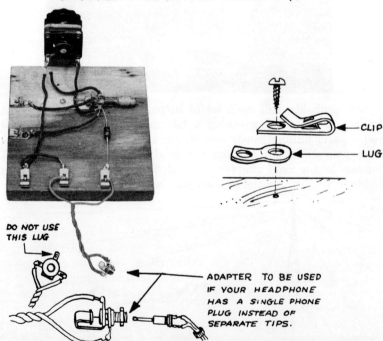

CLIP

LUG

DO NOT USE
THIS LUG

ADAPTER TO BE USED
IF YOUR HEADPHONE
HAS A SINGLE PHONE
PLUG INSTEAD OF
SEPARATE TIPS.

CHAPTER 4

One-Transistor

Headphone Amplifier

With our *One Hour* radio, the signals we hear are simply those picked up by the antenna. The set does nothing to *amplify* them. That is why a good antenna is important. The signal trapped by the antenna is all we hear. The better the antenna, the stronger the signal.

For many years, the only way to amplify a radio signal was to use a radio tube. Designers dreamed of the day they could find a substitute for the tube. For, wonderful as the tube is, it wastes power in the form of heat, and requires complex power and filament supplies. It also suffers from some of the same troubles as the lowly light bulb—including burning out!

Shortly after the end of World War II, technicians at Bell Laboratory, under the direction of Dr. William Shockley, developed the now-familiar transistor. Originally the device was a modification of the germanium diode used in the *One Hour* radio. However, the transistor has one all-important difference: it will function as an amplifier. When a weak radio signal is properly applied to a transistor, a *big* change will result in the output. (To understand this fully, you need a working knowledge of the theory of the atom.) As we saw earlier, once we have *changed* the flow of electrons in a circuit, we have all we need to create sound, or to do many other things.

Furthermore, transistors have other advantages. First of all, they are much smaller, and many of them cost less, than tubes. Even more important, tubes require power transformers, voltages as high as 400 volts, expensive filter capacitors—plus many other power-supply parts. On the other hand, transistors will work with only a flashlight battery or two for power. For this reason, they are safer, too. (You can't get much of a jolt from a couple of small batteries.)

In fact, transistors will do just about anything tubes can do. Even the few exceptions are falling, one by one. Eventually,

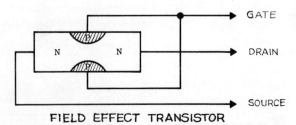

FIELD EFFECT TRANSISTOR

transistors (or modifications like the tunnel diode) will probably replace tubes in almost *every* electronic job. So we might
as well skip tubes for the time being, and start right out with
transistors.

Muscles for Our Crystal Set

We want to make our *One Hour* Radio louder. To do that, we
will put together an amplifier, using only one transistor and a
few parts. Despite its simplicity, the amplifier will step up the
signal from our little radio until it may be so loud on strong stations that we'll have to turn down the volume control.

The single-transistor amplifier is only the first step. By adding a few more parts and two more transistors, we can boost
our signal to where it will operate a speaker.

Enough conversation. Let's buy the parts, haul out the tools,
and build something!

Shopping List

Quantity	Description	In Drawing, Part Labeled:
1	SK3004 transistor or equivalent (2N109)	
6	Fahenstock clips and screws	
7	Soldering lugs (for making con- nection to clips)	
1	470,000 (470K)-ohm 1/2-watt resistor	
1	5600-ohm 1/2-watt resistor	
1	.02-mfd (microfarad) 50-volt (or higher) ceramic-disc ca- pacitor	
1	4-lug terminal strip	

Quantity	Description	*In Drawing,* *Part Labeled:*

1	500,000-ohm transistor potenti-ometer (⅝″ diameter) with SPST (single-pole, single-throw) switch	
1	2-mfd, 12- or 15-volt subminia-ture electrolytic capacitor	
1	Small metal mounting bracket and screws	
1	Miniature knob	

The first step is to prepare a wooden baseboard 5½ inches square, of pine, cedar, redwood, or other soft wood. It should be sanded and then either waxed or varnished.

5-½″ SQUARE BOARD   SAND   WAX

Now mount the parts, following the layout in the photographs and drawings. Note that the volume control is mounted on a small metal bracket made by enlarging the top hole in a metal angle. (It can, of course, be mounted on a piece of hardboard, like the tuning capacitor in the *One Hour* radio.) After mounting the control, slide the knob on and secure it to the shaft with a set screw.

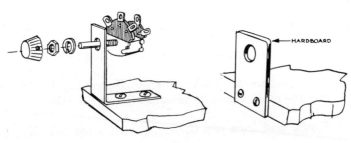

HARDBOARD

Once the parts are mounted, we are ready to wire. As before, use 60/40 solder and push-back hookup wire. Heat your soldering iron; when it is at soldering temperature, wipe it on a damp cloth, so that you begin with a clean, shiny iron.

As before, (S) means solder; and (DS) means make a temporary connection but don't solder, because more leads are still to be added.

Every time you make a connection, check it off in the squares provided. Do this conscientiously, and you will greatly reduce the chance of a wiring error.

We will start at the rear of the baseboard, with clip A in the lower left corner.

☐ Run a lead from clip A (S) to terminal B-3 on the volume control (S).

☐ Connect clip C (S) to clip D (DS).

☐ Run a wire from clip D (S), to terminal-strip lug F-3 (DS).

☐ Connect capacitor E (.02 mfd) from control terminal B-2 (S) to terminal-strip lug F-1 (DS).

☐ Connect control terminal B-4 (S), on the switch at the rear of the control, to terminal-strip lug F-4 (DS).

☐ Wire clip G (S) to control terminal B-5 (S).

☐ Connect lug H (DS) to terminal-strip lug F-2 (DS).

☐ Connect the "plus" lead of capacitor I (2 mfd) to lug H (DS), and run the opposite lead to clip J (S).

☐ Wire resistor K (5.6K) from lug H (S) to clip L (DS).

☐ Connect clip L (S) to terminal-strip lug F-4 (DS).

☐ Hook resistor M (470K) to terminal-strip lug F-4 (S), and run the other end to terminal-strip lug F-1 (DS).

☐ Run a lead from clip C (S), to control lug B-1 (S).

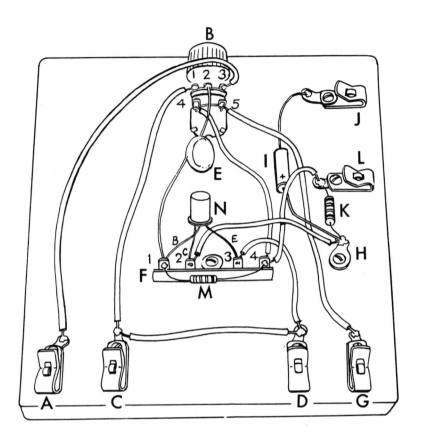

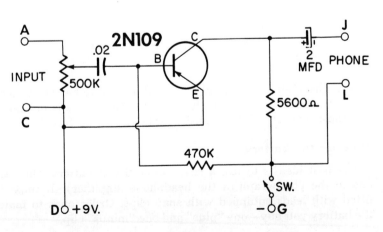

Like germanium diodes, transistors are very rugged except when exposed to too much heat—then they are about as durable as an ice cube. So, while soldering to its leads, we must protect the transistor by grasping each lead with our long-nose

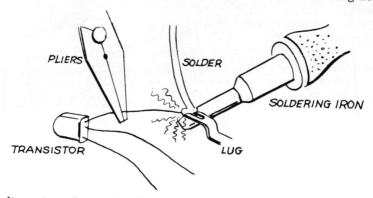

pliers (see drawing). The pliers tend to draw off the heat and thus prevent it from reaching the body of the transistor.

Also be very careful to have the right lead from the transistor. See appendix for data to help you identify leads. Also check the drawings and the base diagram usually packed with the transistor.

☐ Let's hook up the collector lead first. Grasp the lead from the transistor with pliers (as described previously, to protect it from heat), and solder it to terminal-strip lug F-2, which also carries the wire lead from clip H (S).

☐ Next (again using the pliers as heat protection) connect the base transistor lead to terminal-strip lug F-1 (S).

☐ Run the emitter lead of the transistor to lug F-3 and (with pliers to protect the transistor from heat) solder the connection.

Now check and recheck all wiring. If a mistake has been made, the transistor may burn out the moment the battery is hooked to it. Transistors, at a dollar apiece, make *expensive* fuses!

Now for the Battery

The best idea is to use a ready-to-go 9-volt battery (like the one in the photograph of the headphone amplifier). It must be fitted with leads equipped with snap clips. Order ones to match the battery you buy—one "plus" and one "minus" clip.

Notice that the battery has a "plus" terminal—meaning, of course, that the other end is "minus." *This polarity must be observed.* If you reverse the "plus" and "minus" in hooking the battery to the amplifier, the transistor may burn out—*fast.*

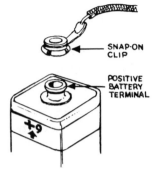

SNAP-ON CLIP

POSITIVE BATTERY TERMINAL

Keeping this hazard in mind, we'll hook the battery to the amplifier. First, turn the volume control to the left as far as it will go. You should feel and hear a click as the switch turns off. Connect the battery to the proper terminals. Note that clip G goes to the *minus* end of the battery, and clip D to the *plus* end.

We're just about ready to go. All we need is a signal (which our *One Hour* radio will supply).

Connect the *One Hour* radio to the amplifier as shown in the photograph. Note that lug D on the *One Hour* radio is connected to lug C on the headphone amplifier, and that lug C goes to lug A on the amplifier. These connections put the signal into the transistor, where it can be amplified.

First of all, be sure the receiver is working properly. Connect the earphone to clips D and C on the *One Hour* radio and tune in a station. If the receiver is working, remove the earphone and connect its terminals to clips J and L on the headphone amplifier.

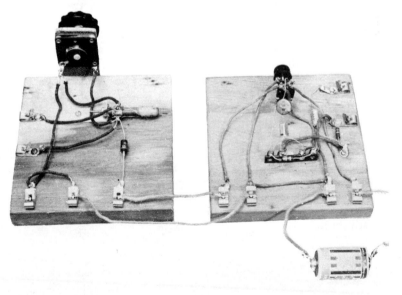

Loud and Clear

Now, hold your breath and snap on the amplifier. If everything is in order, you'll hear the station to which the radio was tuned—only much louder than before. All tuning, of course, is done with the *radio*. The amplifier simply makes the signal stronger.

If you don't hear a sound—even when you give the tuning capacitor a quick twist to cover the whole broadcast band—shut off the amplifier *at once*. Barring a faulty part (unusual with brand-new equipment), you may have a poor solder joint, or you have made a mistake in wiring.

Go back through the written instructions with a colored pencil, checking out *each* lead to make sure you have wired the set exactly as described. Also check the drawing. If you find a wiring error that resulted in the battery polarity being backwards or in the leads from the transistor being improperly connected, correct the error and try the amplifier again.

This time all should be well (unless you were extremely unlucky and burned out the transistor while the amplifier was on). If so, don't feel too bad. The writer remembers when, at the tender age of fifteen, he made a slight mistake in hooking up the battery to an old tube set. As a result, five UV-199 tubes burned out in a sudden flash of blue light. In those days, UV-199 tubes cost $5.00 apiece—and $5.00 would buy about all the groceries one could carry!

It can happen to you . . . you can burn out a transistor. But you shouldn't if you are *careful*.

Chances are your check of the wiring uncovered the trouble and your amplifier plays loud and clear. If not, apply some simple servicing techniques. (See the chapter on "Playing Detective in Electronic Circuits" later in this book.)

Your amplifier *does* play loud and clear? Good! As you will discover quickly if it plays *too* loudly, the volume control works just like the one on any radio. Simply set it to a comfortable listening level.

The amplifier increases the signal from the *One Hour* radio considerably—enough, in fact, that it will drive a power-output stage. This stage, in turn, will operate a speaker with enough volume for the average room. The next chapter discusses such an amplifier. We simply add it to the equipment we have already built.

CHAPTER 5

Speaker
Amplifier Uses
Two Transistors

Practically No Parts

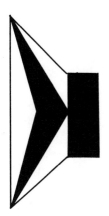

Headphone reception is fine. At best, however, an earphone is an unsociable device, best suited for sneaking in a little listening after the rest of the family has gone to bed. So, sooner or later you will want to build an amplifier that will furnish enough power to operate a speaker.

Such an amplifier will increase the signal from the headphone amplifier sufficiently to operate a speaker on any station which is loud and strong on the headphone unit. A weak signal on the headphone amplifier will also be weak on the speaker amplifier. All the latter does is increase the headphone volume sufficiently to operate a speaker—but good headphone volume must be there to start with.

Just Four 10¢ Resistors

The amplifier uses an extremely simple hookup. It requires only four 10¢ resistors, a few clips, a couple of 10¢ metal angles, a tube socket, and a pair of transistors. One transistor is the low-cost experimenter's type used previously; the other is a power transistor like the one in auto radios. Although power transistors cost more, they take the place of a lot of parts, including transformers.

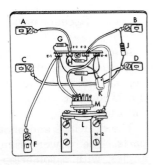

First, the Parts We'll Need

Shopping List

Quantity	Description
1	Power transistor 2N301 or SK-3009
1	2N109 transistor or equivalent (SK 3004)
5	Fahnestock clips
1	4-lug terminal strip
1	6800 (6.8K)-ohm 1/2-watt resistor
1	10,000 (10K) -ohm 1/2 watt resistor
1	240-ohm 1/2-watt resistor
1	100-ohm 1/2-watt resistor
1	Pair of 1-1/2″ × 1-1/2″ metal angle brackets
1	9-prong miniature socket
1	8-ohm speaker (see text)
1	Speaker baffle

In addition to these parts, we will need a baseboard 5-1/2 inches square, just like the ones in the previous units. For the sake of appearance, it should be sanded and waxed or varnished. (Waxing is ideal if you are the eager type—you don't have to wait for it to dry.)

The drawings and photographs show how to mount the various parts. The power transistor is bolted directly to the metal angles, with a soldering lug under one bolt. The metal angles

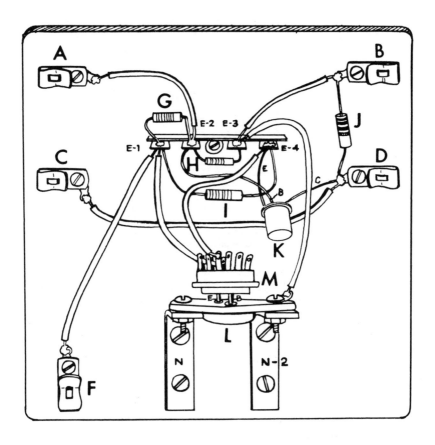

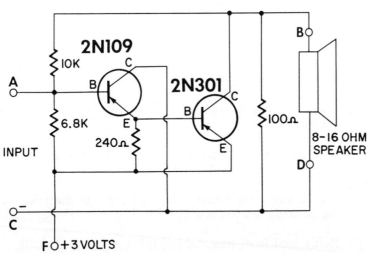

not only support the transistor, but also dissipate the heat it generates. (Incidentally, these angles are available at most hardware stores.) *Important:* Mount the transistor with the "B" prong up (see underside of the transistor).

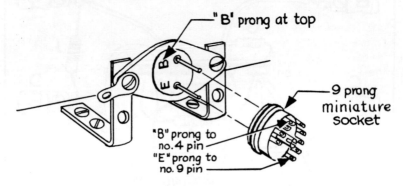

Once everything is mounted, we are ready to begin wiring. As always, use 60/40 solder, a hot, clean, light iron, and pushback hookup wire. Check off each connection on the list as you make it. Remember that (S) means solder, and that (DS) means don't solder—*yet.*

☐ Run a lead from clip A (S) to terminal lug E-2 (DS).

☐ Connect resistor G (6.8K) from terminal lug E-2 (DS) to lug E-1 (DS).

☐ Run a lead from terminal lug E-1 (DS) to clip F (S).

☐ Connect a 3-inch lead to terminal lug E-1 (DS). Leave one end free for later use.

☐ Run resistor I (240 ohms) from terminal lug E-1 (S) to terminal lug E-4 (DS).

☐ Connect a 3-inch lead to terminal lug E-4 (DS). Leave one end free for later use.

☐ Run resistor H (10K) from terminal lug E-2 (DS) to terminal lug E-3 (DS).

☐ Run a lead from terminal lug E-3 (DS) to the soldering lug on angle bracket N-2 (S).

☐ Run a lead from terminal lug E-3 (S) to clip B (DS).

☐ Run resistor J (100 ohms) from clip B (S) to clip D (DS).

☐ Run a lead from clip D (DS) to clip C (S).

Now we're ready to connect the transistors. For the power transistor, we actually connect to two terminals on a 9-prong miniature socket. This provides a practical way to hook onto the transistor without soldering to the short leads and thereby running the risk of damaging the transistor.

Do not make connections to the socket while the transistor is plugged in.

☐ Connect the lead from terminal E-4 to socket pin 4 (reading clockwise, looking at the bottom of socket M) (S).

☐ Connect the lead from terminal E-1 to socket pin 9 (S). Leave the socket off the power transistor for the moment.

☐ Next we'll hook up transistor K. From the diagram packed with the transistor, identify the emitter, base, and collector leads. Protecting the transistor with pliers applied to the lead, hook the collector lead to clip D (S).

☐ Again with pliers to absorb the heat, run the base lead to terminal E-2 (S).

☐ Hook the emitter lead to terminal E-4 (S).

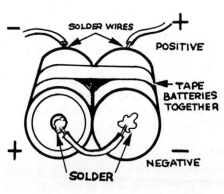

SOLDER WIRES

POSITIVE

TAPE BATTERIES TOGETHER

NEGATIVE

SOLDER

At this point, check and recheck the wiring. We're now using an expensive transistor, so mistakes cost more!

Once everything appears all right, make up a 3-volt battery from two full-sized flashlight cells, as shown in the photograph and in the drawings. (The larger cells insure a more reasonable battery life.)

Vocal Chords for Our Amplifier

Of course, we'll need a speaker. Furthermore, it *must* be one with a fairly high-resistance voice coil—a *minimum* of 8 ohms (12- or 16-ohm units are better). *Don't* let anyone sell you a 3.2-ohm voice-coil speaker. It will not work properly; moreover, it may *destroy* the transistor.

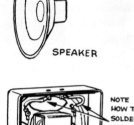

SPEAKER

The speaker shown is a low-priced 8-ohm, 2½-inch unit. Because of its small size, it will not give as much output as a 5-inch or larger speaker. However, it is satisfactory for fairly close-up listening in the average room.

The speaker is mounted in a small plastic baffle, as shown. This is done by drilling holes in the four corners of the front to match the holes on the speaker, and then bolting the speaker to the baffle with small machine screws and nuts.

If a backplate comes with the baffle, *don't* use it because it will

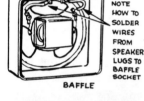

NOTE HOW TO SOLDER WIRES FROM SPEAKER LUGS TO BAFFLE SOCKET

BAFFLE

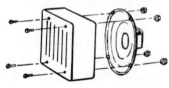

cut down both the volume and the tonal range. (If you use the backplate at all, drill it full of holes. The more holes, the better—which accounts for the advice to leave it off!)

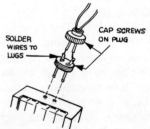

SOLDER WIRES TO LUGS

CAP SCREWS ON PLUG

The baffle shown has a terminal socket in the top, to which the speaker voice-coil leads are wired. A two-wire lead is provided for hooking the speaker to the amplifier. The drawings show how to make connections to the plug going into the terminal socket at the top of the baffle.

(Of course, if you use a larger speaker, you will have to make up some kind of baffle. A wooden box open on one side will do the trick, or you can buy a ready-made speaker baffle from your parts supplier.)

Hooking the Units Together

The photographs and drawings show how to hook the speaker amplifier to the two units built previously. The headphone clips from the headphone amplifier are hooked to the input clips on the speaker amplifier. The same connection also hooks the B— together so that the switch on the headphone amplifier can control the batteries for both units. The "plus" on the 3-volt battery goes to clip F on the speaker amplifier. The speaker goes to output clips B and D.

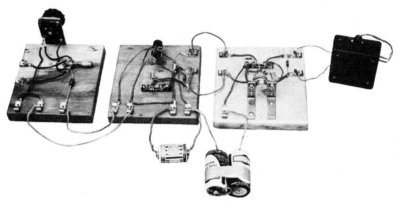

With the switch off, shove the 9-prong socket onto the power transistor. Make *certain* prong B (the base of the transistor) is inserted in socket pin 4, and prong E (the emitter) in socket pin 9! *Be careful*—a mistake here may cost you the transistor.

Now with the switch on and a station tuned in, you should hear something from the speaker. The volume control on the

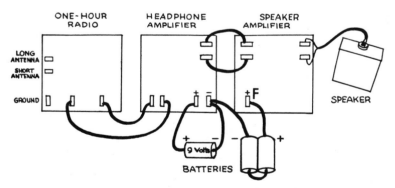

headphone amplifier will control the loudness. Assuming you have a good antenna on your *One Hour* radio and receive good signals on it, you should get satisfactory speaker volume on *local* stations—not window shattering, but sufficient for pleasant listening.

Comments regarding the previous amplifier apply to this one, too. If it doesn't work, look for a wiring error. However, since you are now a veteran of two previous building jobs and this unit is even simpler than the last one, it should play the moment it is turned on.

If not, be certain the amplifier is receiving a signal from the preceding units. You can easily check this by touching the tips of your crystal earphone to input terminals A and C of the amplifier. You should hear the station to which the *One Hour* radio is tuned. If so, you know everything is working up to that point and the trouble is in the amplifier. Check and recheck the amplifier wiring. If that doesn't help, read the later chapter, "Playing Detective in Electronics Circuits."

CHAPTER 6

About Parts

and Symbols

When you are starting out in electronics, pictorial diagrams like those scattered throughout the book are a big help. They make it easy for you to duplicate the original set with a minimum of technical knowledge. But in so doing, they limit you to following specific instructions for a specific set. Later, you will be unable to tackle the many interesting building projects 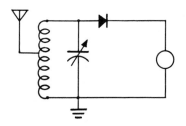 appearing in magazines, along with circuit (schematic), but no pictorial, diagrams. Likewise, you will never be able to do any serious electronic work —for example, radio or TV servicing—or get a general-class radio amateur license. These activities require you to be able to read circuit diagrams.

Actually, most old hands in electronics groan mightily when they have to check through a pictorial diagram. They have found circuit diagrams much easier to read. You will think so, too, once you get the idea.

Late American Sign Language

The various symbols used in electronic circuit diagrams are a kind of shorthand. They look somewhat like the stick drawings of men. Key elements are illustrated in the simplest possible way —just as a stick drawing of a man reduces him to a few lines and circles.

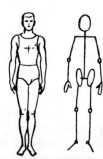

Antennas

Now, let's do the same with an electronic element, an antenna. To do it, we have to go back a few years, to the time when transmitting antennas looked like this—built with wooden spreaders holding a number of wires apart. All wires were tied together into one lead-in.

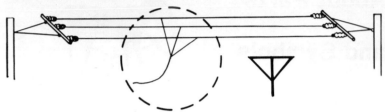

Nobody wanted to draw a whole antenna. So a key element, the triangular feed-line connection, was chosen to indicate an antenna.

All electronic circuit elements are made up in this fashion. A few lines represent, in a crude way, a certain electronic part. Let's get acquainted with some more of them.

Grounds

Originally, just about every electronic device had to have an outside ground like the one on the *One Hour* radio. In those days of insensitive equipment, one could neither receive nor transmit very far without a ground. (Ships at sea depended upon crystal receivers less sensitive than the *One Hour* radio. Their antennas were whoppers — and and the ocean was the ground!)

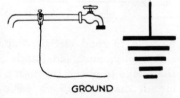

GROUND

As equipment improved, an outside ground was no longer required. However, many parts are connected to a common point, which serves as a kind of ground. Hence, you will find the ground symbol in most circuits. It may indicate connection to a metal chassis or common bus lead, or perhaps to several common points or lugs all wired together.

Wires

So much for antennas and grounds. Now let's look at the wires which tie the various parts together.

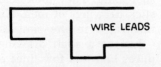

WIRE LEADS

Remembering the sign-language idea, you can see why a wire is simply a straight line. In a typical schematic diagram, most lines either run vertically or horizontally—for no good reason except that they look better and are easier to draw on a drawing board than lines which dive off at some angle.

DOT CONNECTION

When we want to hook two lines together, we need to indicate this. Again we do it in the simplest way possible—with a dot.

In any schematic, one line must almost always cross over another; so we must also indicate *no connection*.

Unfortunately, diagram makers have never quite gotten together on this one. Hence, there are various systems. One is to simply

NO DOT
NO CONNECTION

cross the lines, leaving off the dot. The other is to put a small hump in one of the lines. The latter, although a bit clearer, takes more time on the drafting board, which probably accounts for the fact that the first system seems to be used more. Some-

NO CONNECTION

times a dot is not used at all. A connection is indicated by the lines crossing over, and a hooked line indicates no connection.

Carbon Resistors—And the Secret Code

Now, let's look at some actual parts. One of the most common is the resistor. Again, a simple kind of sign language was developed. A zigzag path offers "resistance" to movement. Since a resistor offers resistance to electrons, we use a zigzag line to indicate a resistor.

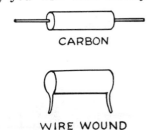
RESISTOR

Resistors come in two basic types—carbon and wirewound. Both serve much the same purpose, the difference being in the wattage they can handle without burning up. In transistor circuits, you will work mostly with carbon resistors (like the one at the right) because the current is low in most circuits. Such resistors are rated in wattage (½ watt, 1 watt, etc.) as well as in resistance.

CARBON

Resistors have always been tiny devices and—like everything else in electronics—are getting

WIRE WOUND

smaller all the time. So, the manufacturers have had to devise some way of indicating their resistance values, *without* depending upon letters or numbers. Even if the printing were big enough to be readable, it usually will burn off the first time the resistor warms up a little. This makes it tough for the service technician to replace the resistor, because he can't tell what its resistance value should be merely by looking at it.

The answer is a system of color coding, with bands of color running around the resistor. (Some resistors have the value stamped on them, along with the color code.) The system has undergone some modification from time to time. Hence, in an old radio you may find a resistor which does not conform to the present method. But the parts you buy today, or find in any sets built within the past few years, will use the same system.

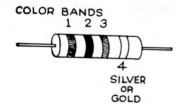

COLOR BANDS
1 2 3

4
SILVER
OR
GOLD

Actually, the system is simple. Each band indicates a number (or string of zeros), depending upon the color. The first three bands may be any of nine different colors. The fourth band (if used) ordinarily is silver or gold. In "decoding" a resistor, the figure is read *toward* the silver or gold band. If a fourth band is not used, the figure is read from the band closest to one end of the resistor.

Here is a table of the colors, plus the numbers they indicate:

Color	First Band	Second Band	Third Band
Black	—	0	—
Brown	1	1	0
Red	2	2	00
Orange	3	3	000
Yellow	4	4	0,000
Green	5	5	00,000
Blue	6	6	000,000
Violet	7	7	0,000,000
Gray	8	8	00,000,000
White	9	9	000,000,000

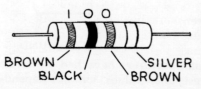

1 0 0

BROWN
BLACK
SILVER
BROWN

Let's take some examples. Suppose our resistor has a brown first band, a black second band, and a brown third band. Referring to our table, we can quickly determine the resistance.

See how it works? Let's try another one. This time we have a red first band, black second band, and green third band.

Add two commas to the above and it will be a bit clearer—2,000,000 ohms. This is a common value. However, to save space, it is usually written *2 megohms*. (*Megohm* means *million* ohms.) It is often abbreviated still further—for example, 2 meg. Sometimes frac-

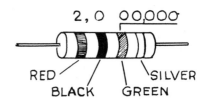

tions are used: ½ meg means one-half million, or 500,000, ohms.

Values under 1,000,000, and 1,000 or over, are often written with the symbol K (K means 1,000). Thus, a 1K resistor is a 1,000-ohm resistor. A 500,000-ohm resistor may be written as either 500K or ½ meg.

What about the fourth band on a resistor? This silver or gold band (sometimes omitted) indicates the tolerance of the resistor. The resistors you will be working with usually will have a silver band, which means a tolerance of 10%. Thus a 1,000-ohm (1K) resistor with a silver end-band is within 10% *plus* (1,000 plus 100, or 1,100 ohms) or 10% *minus* (1,000 minus 100, or 900 ohms). So, a 1,000-ohm resistor with a silver end-band may actually measure anywhere from 900 to 1,100 ohms. This is close enough in most circuits.

In key spots in television sets, gold-band resistors with a tolerance of 5% may have to be used. Resistors with no tolerance band need not be avoided. The absence of a fourth band merely means the tolerance is 20%.

Wirewound Resistors

Since wirewound resistors are usually much bigger than carbon resistors, their values are stamped right on the resistor, or on the carton. The printing on the resistor may burn off, of course, should the resistor become too hot. When this happens, the service technician hauls out a Howard W. Sams PHOTOFACT

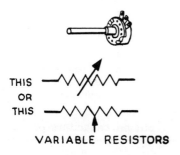

VARIABLE RESISTORS

diagram and finds out from it what the part should be. You can see what a fix he would be in if he *couldn't* read a schematic!

So far, all we have talked about are non-adjustable items—once in the set, they retain (we hope!) the same value. Of course, there are also adjustable components, usually capacitors and resistors. The volume control on a radio is a good example of a variable resistor. Note that we indicate it with the regular resistor symbol, and then use an arrow to show that it is adjustable. The arrow technique is used on other parts, too, as you will see later.

Capacitors

Capacitors (sometimes called *condensers*) are another key building block in electronic circuits. These components come in many shapes and sizes. The more common ones are shown in the drawings. Some, such as ceramic and mica, for example, are often used interchangeably; this fact is usually indicated in the parts list which accompanies a construction article. Paper capacitors are not as versatile as ceramic and mica types, and electrolytic capacitors are used only for certain specialized jobs.

TUBULAR CERAMIC

DISC CERAMIC

CAPACITORS

.1 mfd 600 VOLT

PAPER

8.8 mfd 400 VOLT

All capacitors are made up of "plates" separated by a layer of insulating material (which may even be air). Hence, the symbol for a capacitor is two lines separated by space. Should the capacitor be an electrolytic, it will have polarity, like a battery. The polarity is usually shown by the schematic symbol.

As you will discover in looking at circuit diagrams, capacitors may also be shown with one line slightly curved. The curved line indicates the side of the capacitor going to the grounded side of the circuit.

For awhile, capacitors were color coded. However, the system was so confusing that, much to everybody's relief, *most* (but unfortunately not *all*) capacitors today have the value stamped right on them. Since capacitors seldom heat up much (except electro-

ELECTROLYTIC CAPACITOR

TO GROUND SIDE OF CIRCUIT

lytics, on occasion), the markings stay put on capacitors pretty well.

One Millionth of a Millionth

The value (electrical size) of a capacitor is not simple to show because, like resistors, there is more than one way to indicate the same size.

The first consideration is voltage rating, which is easy—for example, a capacitor may be rated at 15 volts for use in transistor circuits. This rating is the maximum DC voltage the capacitor can withstand without breaking down. For this reason, it is essential to use a capacitor with a voltage rating *higher* than is likely to be encountered in the set. In a transistor set with 9 volts, the capacitors will often be rated at 12 or 15 volts— just to allow a safety margin.

Now for the electrical value, the microfarad. Actually, the basic electrical unit is the farad. However, a capacitor with a capacity of one farad might be as big as a bathtub! So, the largest capacitor you are likely to encounter will be rated in *micro*farads. A *micro*farad (abbreviated *mfd—m* for *micro* and *fd* for *farad*) is *one-millionth* of a farad.

Electrolytic capacitors are usually one or more microfarads. With paper or ceramic capacitors, the usual rating is in a decimal of a microfarad. A common size is .01 mfd. Everything would be just fine if all capacitors were rated thusly. As they get smaller, however, a new system takes over.

For example, a common size of ceramic or mica capacitor is .00025 mfd. This value may also be expressed in another way— in *micro*microfarads (mmf). This is one millionth *of* one millionth of a farad—pretty small indeed!

To reduce a parts value like .00025 mfd to *micro*microfarads, we must multiply it by one million. If you remember how to work decimals, the job is easy. For example:

$$.00025 \times 1,000,000 = 250 \text{ mmf}$$

Likewise, you can go the other way. To translate 500 mmf into mfd, we simply divide 500 by 1,000,000. For example:

$$500 \div 1,000,000 = .0005 \text{ mfd}$$

If that seemed complicated, don't despair. The reason is that you probably don't use decimals very often. Fortunately, you can quickly learn to do the job mentally by adding zeros. Hence, to go from .00025 mfd to 250 mmf, simply move the decimal point six places to the *right;* to go from 250 mmf to .00025 mfd, move the decimal point six places to the *left.*

As a last resort, you can always show your shopping list to the counterman at the radio parts distributor. He has to understand the markings in order to sell capacitors!

Variable Capacitors

Just as with resistors, an arrow indicates a variable capacitor. It may be drawn through the capacitor symbol (indicating a tuning capacitor), or the curved plate may be terminated with an arrow (indicating a trimmer). Tuning capacitors are usually packed in a box, with the size stamped on the side of the box. Since they are almost always labeled in mmf, no translating job is needed. Note that the rotor is the set of variable plates, and that the stator is the stationary plates.

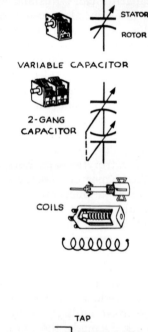

VARIABLE CAPACITOR

2-GANG CAPACITOR

COILS

Coils

Coils are easy to indicate in a schematic—you simply draw what looks like a pig's tail.

A variable coil is indicated by an arrow, as shown in the drawing. If the coil is tapped, the tapped connection is also shown. The three parallel lines indicate the core.

The rating of the coil is the *henry*. Except for audio and filter chokes, however, the coils and RF chokes (a specialized type of coil) you encounter will be rated

TAP

ADJUSTABLE WITH TAP

mostly in millihenrys or microhenrys. The box is usually stamped with the value, so ordering parts is easy. Be certain never to mix up the *milli* and the *micro*—the difference is very large indeed. A millihenry is equal to one-thousandth, and a microhenry to one-millionth, of a henry.

Transformers

Transformers are simply coils with cores, usually of iron. The core is indicated by three lines, as shown in the drawing. Transformers often have a number of

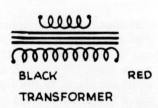

BLACK   RED

TRANSFORMER

windings, identified by color coding the various leads. This color code is very important—follow it carefully.

Diodes and Transistors

Transistors are so numerous and complex that to even try to indicate the possible types which are (or will be) available is impossible. The diagrams at the right illustrate the two types found in this book. Notice that the symbols for the NPN and PNP types differ *only* in the direction the arrows point.

Sometimes the manufacturer changes the arrangement of the leads after a transistor has been in production for awhile. If the transistor you buy doesn't have the same terminal arrangement as the ones in this book, check it carefully against the base diagram (usually packed with the transistor). If the matter *still* isn't entirely clear, see a transistor manual. (Such manuals are issued from time to time by transistor manufacturers.) The idea, of course, is to be able to identify *collector, base,* and *emitter* leads.

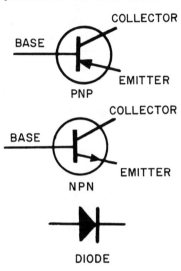

Tubes

Although the sets in this book do not use tubes, you will want to be able to recognize a tube symbol when one comes your way. Tubes are of many different designs—to diagram them all would require many pages. All tube manuals give the type numbers, characteristics, schematic symbols, and base connections of the tubes. (You should buy one of the manuals. They are inexpensive and worth far more than their nominal cost.)

Phones

The symbol for a headphone is one of the simplest of all, particularly for only a single phone. The symbol for a pair of phones is almost as simple.

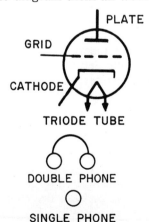

Switches

Switches are easily indicated, too. A switch often has multiple sections, all acting at the same time when the switch is turned. A multiple-section switch is shown. Notice how the units are tied together with a dotted line, indicating that they are all operated by the same button or from the same shaft. The same technique is used with variable capacitors and resistors, for example, in which several components are controlled by the same shaft.

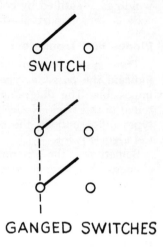

SWITCH

GANGED SWITCHES

Other Common Parts

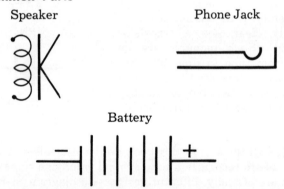

Speaker

Phone Jack

Battery

Once you have become acquainted with the appearance of the various parts and their symbols, your next step is to fit the pieces together and apply this sign language in drawing and reading actual circuit diagrams. This we will do in the following chapter.

CHAPTER 7

Reading

Circuits

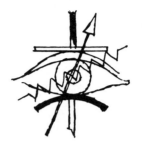

Once you understand the various symbols for electronic parts, you will have gone far toward being able to read circuits. In addition, there are certain tricks of the trade you will need to know.

As a starting point, let's look at the pictorial diagram for the *One Hour* radio—about as simple an electronic device as you will ever encounter.

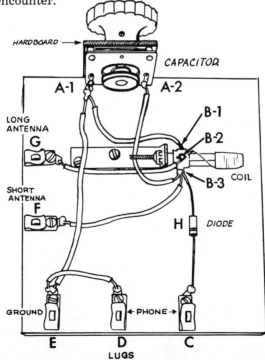

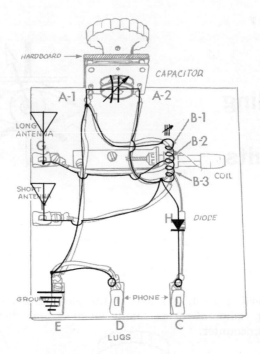

We'll begin with the pictorial diagram itself, just to get oriented. On top of it, let's lay the symbols indicating the different parts.

A lot of things become apparent in a hurry. For example, the symbol for the antenna goes to the Fahnestock clip to which the antenna is normally connected (the symbol illustrates the purpose of the clip). The same is true of the ground; notice that the ground terminal goes to the ground clip.

A circuit drawing superimposed upon the pictorial diagram would be something of a rat race to follow. With a little rearranging, however, we can draw a circuit (Drawing 1) that follows the same general layout, but is a lot easier to read.

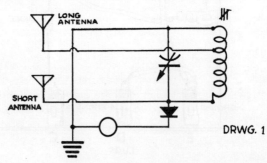

DRWG. 1

We could stop at this point, for we have a schematic which anyone with electronic experience could use for wiring equipment. But let's go one step further and draw still another diagram (Drawing 2), more in keeping with the ones you will actually encounter.

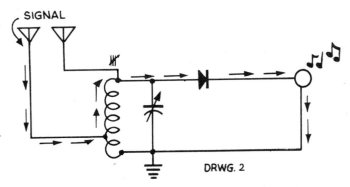

At first glance, this new diagram looks completely different from the first one. However, if you will trace the wiring out, lead for lead, you will discover that it is exactly the same electrically—the difference is simply in the arrangement of the parts.

Why the difference?

Read From Left to Right

Reading circuits on complicated equipment (for example, television sets) could be a pretty formidable job if there weren't some sort of pattern to follow. Such a pattern was arrived at many years ago; essentially, it is just like reading. You mentally follow the radio signal through the diagram—your eyes moving from left to right, just as they do in reading this page.

In our *One Hour* radio, the signal enters the antenna, goes to the coil, then to the diode where it is detected, and finally to the earphone. In the diagram, therefore, we lay out the parts so we can follow the signal path from left to right.

At this point, don't worry if you can't look at a circuit and instantly visualize what is happening; this skill will come later. However, it *is* important to remember that the left side of a circuit diagram is the *input* and the right side is the *output*.

Some other things are often puzzling to the beginner. For example, *within* the wiring of a set there often are several points where wires can be joined without upsetting the circuit in any way.

Let's go back to the pictorial diagram. Notice the lead from coil terminal B-1 to variable capacitor terminal A-1, and the lead from A-1 to ground clip E.

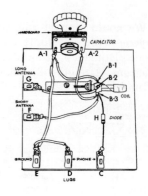

The lead from ground clip E could just as well have gone to B-1 on the coil, instead of to A-1; *electrically* it would have made no difference. The only reason for the layout shown is that running the wire to A-1 is more convenient *mechanically* than fishing the wire lead around the coil.

Let's take another example.

In the pictorial diagram, diode H is connected between B-3 and clip C. For all practical purposes, the B-3 end of the diode could just as well have gone to clip F instead.

Another possibility is the lead which runs from A-2 to coil lug B-3; it also could have gone to clip F. It wouldn't be the best practice to do so, since tuning capacitor leads should be as short as possible; but on a low-frequency set like this one, it would make little practical difference.

Why can we play fast and loose with the wiring?

If you will look at the schematic again, you will find one end of the diode, the short antenna, and one side of the variable capacitor connected to the same point *electrically*.

Notice in the three diagrams that capacitor A-2 *could* be connected to the top of coil B-3, at some midpoint between B-3 and diode H, or directly on the end of diode H. The result would be the same.

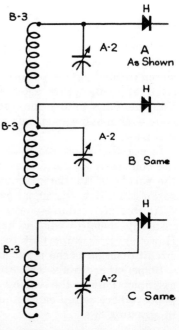

As you become better acquainted with schematics — and with comparing circuit diagrams with the actual wiring — you'll find time and again that the reason behind a wiring layout is usually mechanical. For example, in sets with tubes, the tube socket lugs are convenient spots onto which parts can be mounted.

Hence, any given lug may have several parts hooked onto it, because the builder is invariably looking for something solid on which he can mount the part. In noncritical portions of the circuit, this may be six inches from where you would think it would be by just looking at the diagram.

At first glance, don't expect a schematic to look like the wiring—it seldom will. As an example, in most radios the on-off switch is combined with a volume control; so the two are actually *one* part. In drawing up a circuit, however, the volume control usually is some distance from the on-off switch, and may or may not be hooked to it with a dotted line to indicate that they are two segments of the same part.

Besides, in wiring, the builder virtually *never* taps wire leads to hook in a part, as you might expect by looking at a circuit diagram. When he wants to tie one wire to another, the usual meeting place is some type of soldering lug, terminal strip, or tube or transistor socket.

For practice, let's try another one—

The headphone amplifier has more parts than the *One Hour* radio. So let's try translating the pictorial diagram into a schematic diagram.

Again we will superimpose the schematic diagram over the pictorial diagram (Drawing 3). Even with the pictorial diagram removed (Drawing 4), the schematic gets pretty confusing, with leads going in all directions. In fact, if schematics had to be drawn this way, we'd probably still be listening to crystal sets!

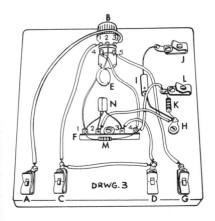
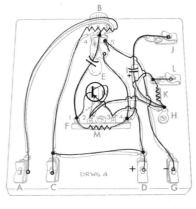

Redrawing the diagram in an orderly way clears matters up quite a bit, as you will see from Drawing 5. However, the diagram can be made still simpler and more conventional, as shown in Drawing 6.

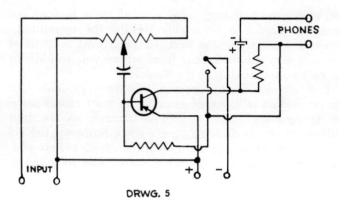

DRWG. 5

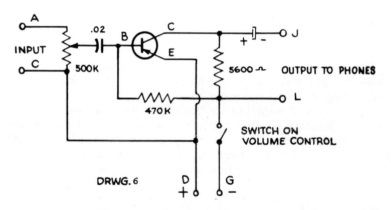

DRWG. 6

The two small units covered in this chapter do not, of course, illustrate all the parts you will encounter in building electronic equipment. However, if you have taken the time to study the *method* of preparing circuits, as outlined in this chapter, you will be able to "dope out" more complicated circuits without much trouble. Before long, like all old hands at electronics, you will regard schematics as easy—and pictorial drawing as tough!

CHAPTER 8

Easy
Pocket
Radio

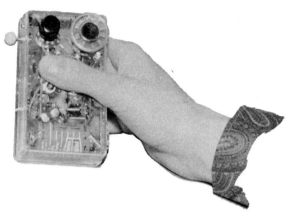

Now that we have learned to read circuits and diagrams, we could start out by building gear from the schematics alone. However, pictorial diagrams do make things easier until mentally translating circuit symbols into parts becomes second nature. By continually building equipment, comparing the circuit and pictorial diagrams as you work, you will get the hang of things quite painlessly and quickly. So this set—as well as all others in this book—is represented with *both* schematic and pictorial diagrams.

It is always best to start with the schematic, because it gives you the "big picture" at a glance. With this idea in mind, let's study the circuit for this simple pocket radio.

First, though, a word about pocket radios.

50 Feet of Wire Won't Fit Your Pocket

In designing any pocket set, the builder is faced with a dilemma. If he makes the set extremely simple, it is pocket sized all right—but it will require a 50-foot outside antenna. (Yes, such sets have been described in "how-to-do-it" articles, and some have even been manufactured!)

On the other hand, if the designer piles in enough parts that the set has plenty of sensitivity to work *without* an antenna, he has to be careful lest he create a design so tough to build, and so expensive, that it would be better to go out and buy a manufactured unit.

Rather than such a set, let's build one which—although *not* able to work without some kind of makeshift antenna—is sensitive enough to require only a small antenna. The set will pull in all the stronger local stations when clipped to the finger stop on a telephone, a metal lamp, the downspout on a gutter, a metal fence, a bed spring—or just about any sizable piece of metal.

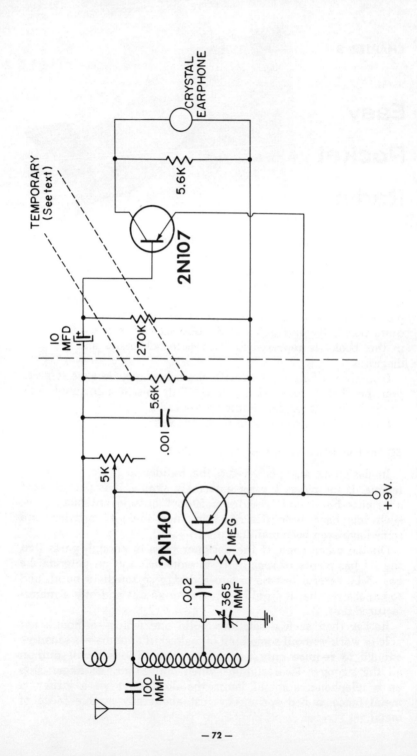

The set works much better with a regular outside antenna, of course, and at night will pull in stations hundreds of miles away. Furthermore, it contains standard parts, most of which can be used in the more complicated pocket set described later on.

Now, let's look at the circuit of our "easy" pocket radio.

First of all, note the transistors. In the units described so far, the transistors have all been of the audio type, designed to amplify the signal *after* it has been detected. This set uses a

radio-frequency transistor for one of the two stages in the circuit. (Transistors of this type can detect as well as amplify an incoming radio-frequency signal.) This extra "push" helps give some of the sensitivity we need to get along without much of an antenna.

Dog-Chasing-Tail Electronics

In addition, we will use a circuit trick known as *regeneration*. Regeneration makes it possible for us to use part of the incoming signal to reinforce the signal just behind it—a kind of dog-chasing-tail technique that adds to the sensitivity. This gain is achieved with some inconvenience: the set must be operated carefully, or else it will squeal. However, the extra sensitivity is well worth that small disadvantage.

The RF transistor, a 2N140 or equivalent, is low in cost, yet reliable. It is used as a regenerative detector, resistance-coupled to a 2N109 transistor which serves as an audio amplifier. Note from the schematic that the detector and audio stages are separated by a dashed line, so you can easily tell which is which.

To get started, we'll need some parts. Here is the list:

Shopping List

Quantity	Description	In Drawing Part Labeled:
1	Flat ferrite tapped antenna coil 2⅜" long for use with 365-mmf variable capacitor	L
1	10-365 mmf transistor-type miniature tuning capacitor with dial	A
1	5000-ohm potentiometer (5/8" diameter transistor type) with spst switch	C
1	.002-mfd ceramic-disc capacitor	G
1	.0001-mfd (100-mmf) ceramic-disc capacitor	B
1	.001-mfd ceramic-disc capacitor	I
1	2N140 transistor or equivalent (2N219, GE-1, SK3005)	T
1	2N107 transistor or equivalent (SK3003)	N
2	5600 (5.6K)-ohm 1/2-watt resistor	J, M
1	1-meg 1/2-watt resistor	F
1	270,000 (270K)-ohm 1/2-watt resistor	L
2	Snap-on battery clips, one "plus" and one "minus" for 9-volt transistor battery	P, Q
1	9-volt transistor-type battery	
1	Small box 6-32 machine screws and nuts	
1	10-mfd 15-volt electrolytic capacitor	K

Shopping List (cont'd)

Quantity	Description	In Drawing, Part Labeled:
1	Plastic box, $2\frac{3}{4}'' \times 4\frac{1}{2}'' \times 1\frac{3}{16}''$	
3	4-lug terminal strips	
1	Knob for volume control	
1	Miniature plug and jack with 6-foot antenna hank	
1	Insulated test clip	R
1	Small coil of flexible indoor antenna wire (*wire*, not tinsel)	

With the parts at hand, the next step is to put them together. We'll start by mounting three 4-lug terminal strips, using 6-32 machine screws and nuts. The position of the terminal strips is determined largely by the 9-volt battery. The idea is to mount them so the battery just barely slips in between the ter-

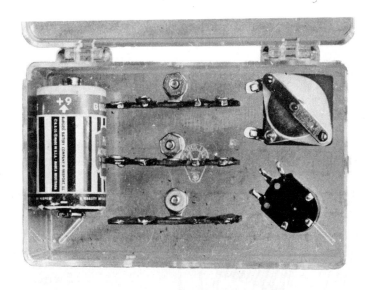

minal strips and the end of the box. In this way, the battery will be fairly well anchored when the lid is closed.

In similar fashion, mount the variable capacitor close to the top of the box, so the antenna coil will just barely slide in (see subsequent photographs, which show this coil in place). Mount the capacitor to the box by drilling a hole of suitable

size. The location of the variable resistor (volume control) is not critical. You can mount it "by eye," in the approximate position shown in the photograph, again drilling a hole of the proper size.

Drill three more holes: one for the antenna jack, mounted on the side of the box (see photograph); one for the soldering lug, used to secure the coil to the box; and one for the headphone cord.

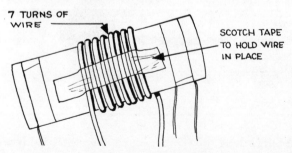

7 TURNS OF WIRE

SCOTCH TAPE TO HOLD WIRE IN PLACE

First of all, we'll need to add a "tickler" winding to coil L. This consists of seven turns of wire, put on as shown in the drawing, and anchored with

Scotch tape. Flexible wire should be used here. Stranded indoor antenna wire (*wire,* not the cheap tinsel-covered fabric some-times sold for the purpose) is ideal, since it can also be used as hookup wire for all the wiring in the set. For compact sets like this one, this highly flexible antenna wire is easier to use than regular hookup wire.

Next, we will wire. As before, use a small, hot, pencil-type iron and 60/40 solder. (As you know by now, "S" means solder; "DS" means don't solder yet, but simply connect the parts to-gether and solder later.)

- [ ] Run coil lead L-1 to capacitor lug A-2 (DS).

- [ ] Run coil lead L-2 to capacitor lug A-1 (DS).

- [ ] Connect one lead of capacitor B (100 mmf) to A-2 (S), and the other to jack H (S).

- [ ] Connect coil lead L-3 to terminal-strip lug J-1 (DS).

- [ ] Connect one lead of capacitor G (.002 mfd) to J-1 (S), and the other to J-2 (DS).

- [ ] Connect resistor F (1 meg) between J-2 (DS) and ter-minal-strip lug E-1 (DS).

- [ ] Hook a lead from E-1 (DS) to terminal-strip lug D-1 (DS).

- [ ] Connect resistor J (5.6K) between D-1 (DS) and D-2 (DS).

- [ ] Connect capacitor I (.001 mfd) between D-1 (DS) and D-2 (DS).

- [ ] Connect a 6-inch lead to D-1 (DS). Leave the other end free.

- [ ] Connect a lead between D-1 (S) and A-1 (S).

- [ ] Connect coil lead L-5 to D-2 (DS).

- [ ] Connect a lead between D-2 (DS) and variable-resistor lug C-4 (S).

- [ ] Connect a 6-inch lead to D-2 (S). Leave the other end free.

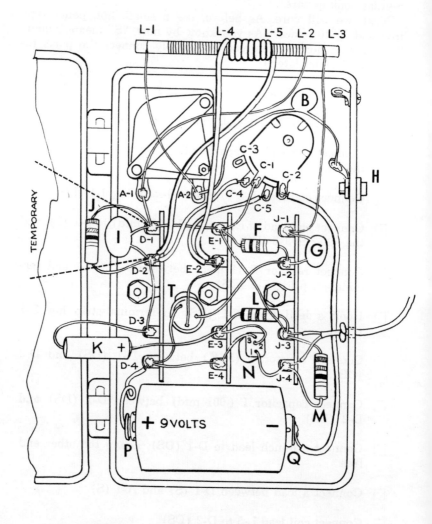

☐ Run a lead from C-5 (S) to E-2 (DS).

☐ Solder the "minus" battery-terminal clip onto a wire lead. Run the lead to C-2 (S).

☐ Run a lead from C-1 (S) to E-1 (S).

☐ Hook coil lead L-4 to E-2 (DS).

☐ Run a lead from D-4 (DS) to E-4 (DS).

☐ Hook a lead to terminal lug D-4 (DS). On the other end of the lead, solder the "plus" battery-terminal clip.

This completes the first part of the wiring, except for the transistor. As described in previous chapters, the transistor

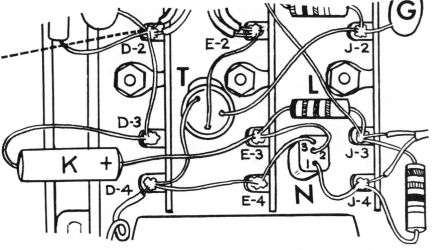

should be handled with kid gloves. Use your long-nose pliers to protect it from heat. To identify the leads, see the diagram packed with the transistor and appendix of this book.

☐ Turn transistor T (2N140 or equivalent) upside down, and run the base lead to lug J-2 (S).

☐ Run the emitter lead to D-4 (S).

☐ Run the collector lead to E-2 (S).

☐ Connect insulated test clip R to the far end of the 6-foot antenna wire.

Testing as You Build

Home-built equipment is actually much harder to troubleshoot than manufactured gear. You know a manufactured unit worked at one time. The only problem is to find out why it quit. With homemade equipment you lack the same comforting assurance!

For that reason, many experienced builders wire only one stage at a time, and *test as they go*. Thus, if the builder runs into trouble, he knows it is in *one* stage; he doesn't have to look for it throughout the whole set. With this useful idea in mind, we have designed all equipment in this book so you can test as you build.

To see how this works, let's look at the schematic again. Notice that the set is divided into two parts—a detector and an audio stage.

All by itself, the detector picks up the radio signals; the audio stage simply makes them louder. We should be able to hear the output from the detector stage alone—weak perhaps, but there.

The signal from the transistor detector is developed across resistor J (5.6K). Hence, to hear the signal, all we have to do is connect our crystal earphone *across* this resistor.

As shown in the photograph below, hook the earphone to the two leads from D-1 and D-2 (which are connected to each side of the resistor). Next, hook up the battery and plug in the antenna lead. For test purposes, hook the insulated antenna clip onto whatever antenna is available (preferably a good one, like the 90-foot **L** described previously).

Next, turn on the switch and advance the volume control (actually the regeneration control) approximately halfway. Then rotate the variable capacitor.

If everything is working all right, you will hear sharp whistles as you tune across the dial. Each whistle indicates a station. By backing off the regeneration control, you can stop the whistle and thus make the station intelligible. You will find the set most sensitive *just before* the whistling begins.

Should the set not work as described, check the wiring carefully against both the pictorial and the schematic diagram. With a colored pencil, go over each lead on the drawing. Also check each connection, to be certain the solder joint is good.

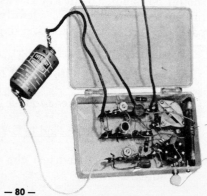

If the set seems to be "alive"—that is, you receive a few weak signals, but no whistles—the detector is probably not oscillating because coil L-4 is not polarized properly. This is easily corrected by switching the leads to the "tickler" coil. Shift lead L-4 from E-2 to D-2, and move L-5 to E-2 (L-5 formerly went to D-2). If the set *still* refuses to oscillate (whistle), increase the number of turns on coil L-4–L-5. This should clear up any remaining trouble. If not, read the chapter on servicing later on in the book.

Once the detector stage is working, the final step is to wire the audio amplifier. This unit steps up the signal sufficiently that we can get along with a very small antenna.

Disconnect the battery before starting to wire.

☐ Clip off the temporary lead soldered to D-1.

☐ Shorten the temporary lead connected to D-2, and run it to D-3 (DS).

☐ Connect the "plus" lead of capacitor K (10 mfd) to E-3 (DS), and the other lead to D-3 (S).

☐ Connect resistor L (270K) between E-3 (DS) and J-3 (DS).

☐ Connect resistor M (5.6K) between J-3 (DS) and J-4 (DS).

☐ Run a lead from J-3 (DS) to E-1 (S).

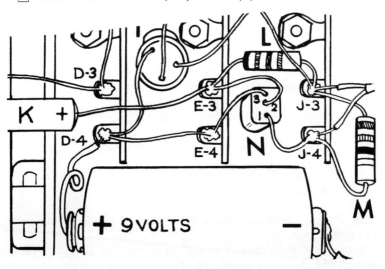

Resistor M is the load resistor for our earphone. The latter must be connected across it, as we did in the detector stage. But first, we must remove the phone tips from the end of the headphone cord. Lay the tip on a piece of wood, and apply your soldering iron to it. When the tip becomes hot, tug *gently* on the headphone cord until it slides out of the end of the tip. Do this with both tips, so you will have wire ends to solder into the set. Take it easy—phone cords are pretty delicate. If you apply too much heat, or pull too hard, you may damage them or short one lead to the other—which will cause some baffling troubleshooting later.

If your earphone has a phone plug, your job is easier. First take the phone plug apart (usually by simply unscrewing the end). You will see the ends of the wire, which you can unsolder.

(Of course, you may fit the case with either a plug jack or headphone jacks, and thus avoid the need for soldering the end of the phone cable. The only advantages of the latter method are to save space and money.)

If you have decided to solder the cord into the set, run it through a hole in the case; then tie a knot, with the knot *inside* the case to take the strain from any tugs on the cord.

☐ Connect one end of the phone cord to J-3 (S). Be *careful* not to heat the wire so much that you melt the insulation and thereby short the wires together (which will make a very dead set, indeed!).

☐ Hook the other phone-cord lead to J-4 (DS).

This completes the wiring, except for transistor N (2N107 or equivalent). Identify the emitter, base, and collector leads.

☐ Using your pliers as before to protect the transistor from heat, connect the emitter lead to E-4 (S).

☐ Connect the base lead to E-3 (S).

☐ Connect the collector lead to lug J-4 (S).

(*Careful*—don't short out the phone leads; see the previous mention.)

As always, check and recheck the wiring, carefully inspecting all connections.

Hook up the battery. Connect antenna clip R to the finger stop on the dial of a telephone. Then tune in the set. It should act much the same as before. The only difference will be a considerably louder signal, thanks to the amplifying qualities of the transistor audio-amplifier stage.

Of course, the telephone dial stop is only one possibility for an antenna. Any length of wire or metal structure should provide satisfactory results. For example, the original model of the set pulled in a half dozen local stations when the antenna lead was clipped to the handle bars of a bicycle.

CHAPTER 9

So You Would

Like to Broadcast

Deep in the heart of almost every person is the secret urge to "go on the air." With this two-transistor broadcasting station you can do exactly that—broadcast over the radio!

Of course, to stay on the right side of the law, you must keep the transmitting range down; otherwise, you will need a federal license. With this idea in mind, we have designed the following home broadcaster to have a range of no more than 50 feet or so (depending upon its antenna and ground, and the sensitivity of the radio to which it is tuned).

This transmitting range is more than ample for you to go on the air and amuse—and perhaps puzzle—your friends. For example, by placing the broadcaster in the next room from a radio to which others are listening, you can break in with a few "important news announcements" of your own! It is a great gadget for parties. Everybody can get into the act and make like a disc jockey.

Unlike most such units, which transmit on only one fixed frequency, this one covers virtually the entire broadcast band. You simply tune it in, using a radio dial knob, to any point on the dial of the radio you are using for the pickup.

The transistors in the unit are of two types. One, a 2N170 NPN RF unit, is the kind frequently used in "home-brewed" pocket radios. The other, a 2N107 PNP AF unit, is used as a modulator. It is so similar to the CK722 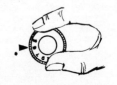 transistors of the sets described earlier that you may borrow a CK722 from one of them.

One word about the unit before we build it. Essentially, the home broadcaster is a self-excited oscillator, plus a modulator driven by a microphone. The oscillator sends out the radio waves, just as a broadcasting station does. These waves are picked up by a nearby radio. Except for a slight rushing noise, however, you won't hear much by listening to the oscillator alone. By adding a modulator (simply an audio amplifier, similar to the headphone amplifier), we can supply a voice signal which hitchhikes onto the radio waves.

Low-Cost Mike

A crystal microphone like the ones for home recorders is ideal for picking up the voice signal. Actually, the home broad-caster will give satisfactory results with even a crystal headphone used as a microphone. Ideally, the headphone should be one of the type shown, with a removable earpiece so a mouthpiece can be screwed on. The mouthpiece increases the pickup, which is quite small because of the small diaphragm on the earphone.

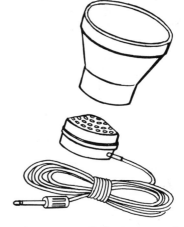

The broadcaster is designed so you can wire the oscillator portion first and get it working, and then finish by wiring the modulator stage. As mentioned previously, this technique of splitting the circuit work into sections for test-as-you-go wiring saves a lot of trouble later, should you have to find a defect. (You *know* right off the bat that the trouble has to be in the stage you are working on.)

To get started on the home broadcaster, first round up the the parts. As you check this shopping list, you will find many of the parts are the same as before. So, if you don't mind tearing down the previous units, you can get a good head start on this one.

Shopping List

Quantity	Description	In Drawing, Part Labeled:
3	Fahnestock clips	A, B, C
1	Transistor driver transformer; primary impedance, 10,000 ohms; secondary impedance, 2,000 ohms center tapped (center tap not used)	D

Quantity	Description	In Drawing, Part Labeled:
1	Miniature jack and antenna lead-in plug (with 6 feet of wire)	E
2	Transistor sockets, 3-contact type	F, H
1	Transistor input transformer; primary impedance, 100,000 ohms; secondary impedance, 1,000 ohms	X
1	Miniature jack for phone mike	J
1	365-mmf transistor-type tuning capacitor	K
6	Soldering lugs	
1	Small box 6-32 machine screws	
2	4-lug terminal strips	
1	Box ½″ 2-56 machine screws and nuts	
1	100,000 (100K)-ohm, ½-watt resistor	R
1	82-ohm, ½-watt resistor	L
1	.01-mfd, 50-volt (or higher) ceramic-disc capacitor	U
1	1,000-ohm, ½-watt resistor	V
1	22,000 (22K)-ohm, ½-watt resistor	T
1	Transistor-type high-Q antenna coil for 365-mmf variable capacitor with tap and adjustable ferrite core	G
1	.005-mfd, 50-volt (or higher) ceramic-disc capacitor	S

Quantity	Description	In Drawing, Part Labeled:
2	2-mfd 10-volt (or higher) transistor-type electrolytic capacitors	BB, CC
1	10-mfd 10-volt (or higher) transistor-type electrolytic capacitor	FF
1	270,000 (270K)-ohm, 1/2-watt resistor	DD
1	Small spool of No. 30 enameled wire	
1	$3^{11}/_{16}''$ x $6^{3}/_{4}''$ *Bakelite* board perforated (see template)	
1	2N170 transistor or equivalent (GE-5 or other NPN RF-AF type such as SK3001)	H
1	2N107 transistor or equivalent (SK3003)	Q

Lots of Holes . . . No Drilling

Because of the smallness of the transistor parts—and of the transistors themselves—a heavy metal chassis is unnecessary. Instead, one popular method is to use small, perforated *Bakelite* boards. They not only save a lot of hole drilling, but also make it possible for you to anchor parts to the board itself, since it is insulated. The technique of building on perforated plastic boards is one you will want to learn—and there is no better time than right now. Cutting the board to size is easy. Just follow the actual-sized template at the end of the chapter.

Parts Layout

☐ Mount the $3^{11}/_{16}''$ x $6^{3}/_{4}''$ perforated *Bakelite* board on two wooden cleats $3^{5}/_{8}''$ x $1^{1}/_{4}''$ x $^{3}/_{4}''$. Use very small screws or (easier) small brads.

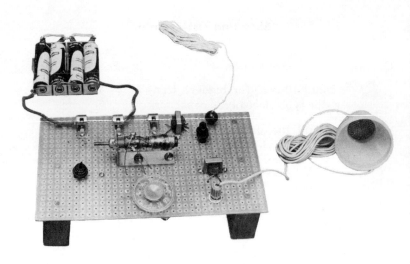

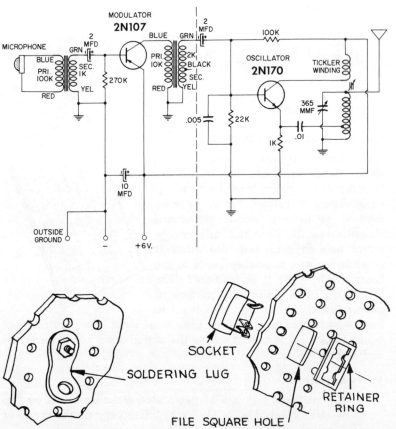

MODULATOR
2N107

MICROPHONE

BLUE
PRI.
100K
RED

GRN
SEC.
1K
YEL

2
MFD

270K

BLUE

PRI.
10K

RED

GRN

2K

BLACK

SEC.
YEL

2
MFD

.005

22K

100K

OSCILLATOR
2N170

TICKLER
WINDING

1K

.01

365
MMF

10
MFD

OUTSIDE
GROUND

—

+6V.

SOCKET

SOLDERING LUG

FILE SQUARE HOLE

RETAINER
RING

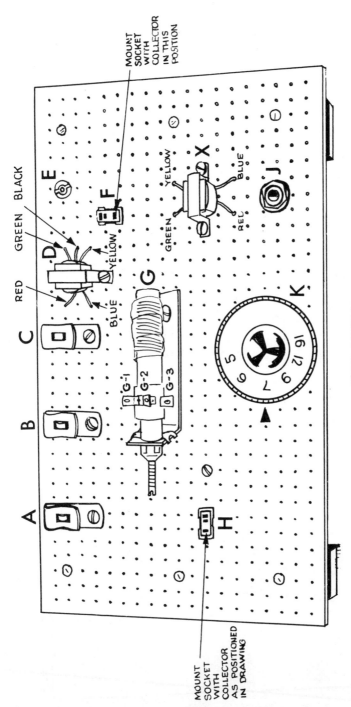

TOP VIEW
PARTS LAYOUT

MOUNT SOCKET WITH COLLECTOR IN THIS POSITION

MOUNT SOCKET WITH COLLECTOR AS POSITIONED IN DRAWING

GREEN BLACK

RED

YELLOW

BLUE

GREEN

YELLOW

RED

BLUE

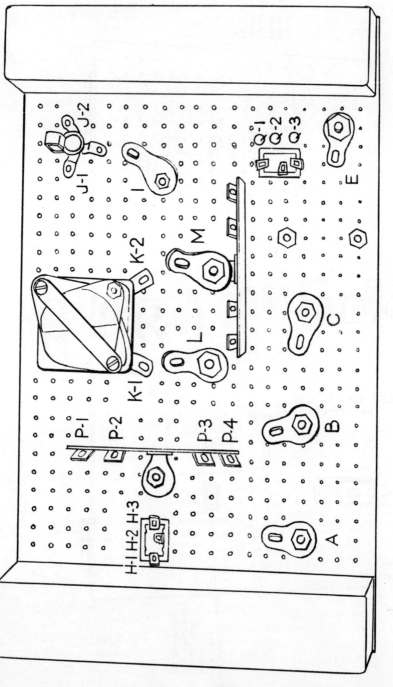

BOTTOM VIEW
PARTS LAYOUT

☐ Slightly enlarge the holes in the perforated board (use the tapered end of your soldering aid tool). Using 2-56 machine screws and hex nuts, mount the three Fahnestock clips (A, B, and C). Be sure that you place a soldering lug under each nut on the bottom of the board.

☐ At the rear of the panel, mount the miniature jack (E) for the antenna lead.

☐ Mount the two transistor sockets (F and H) through a small, square-cornered hole. First, drill a hole with a small drill bit; then enlarge the hole and square the corners with a file. Do not make the hole too large, just large enough for the socket to slip in easily. Secure by forcing on a small metal retainer ring spring (see the drawing).

☐ Mount transformers D and X, using the 2-56 machine screws and nuts. Under one bolt on transformer X, mount soldering lug I. Thread the wire leads from the transformers through any of the suitable holes in the perforated board.

☐ Remove the knob from variable capacitor K. Drill and ream a hole of suitable diameter to carry the shaft, and mount the capacitor on the front of the panel. Secure it to the panel with the mounting nut provided.

☐ Mount the bracket for coil G near the center of the board. Looking at the board from the bottom, note that lug L is mounted under the nut at the left, and that the 4-lug terminal strip O and a single soldering lug M are mounted under the nut at the right.

☐ Mount terminal strip P with a bolt and nut, as indicated.

☐ Mount headphone jack J near the front of the board, in a suitable hole.

All parts in the set are standard except the coil, which must have a tickler winding. The winding consists of 26 turns of No. 30 enameled wire "scramble-wound" over a layer of *Scotch* tape placed over the winding on the coil. The coil should be wound clockwise (looking at it from the end with the adjustment screw). Tape the winding down, and run the leads through the perforated board.

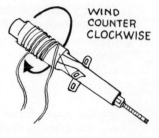

WIND COUNTER CLOCKWISE

Important: The set will not work right unless the coils are properly connected. Unfortunately, the coil you buy may or may not have the exact terminal connection shown. Check the drawing against the diagram packed with the coil to make certain G-1 is the antenna terminal, G-2 is the tap, and G-3 the ground. If not, select for G-1 the terminal the diagram indicates is the tap, etc.

Wiring the Oscillator

With everything mounted, we are ready to start wiring. As before, (S) means solder, (DS) don't solder.

- [ ] Connect the "plus" lead of capacitor FF (10 mfd) to lug A (DS) and the other lead to lug B (DS).

- [ ] Run a lead from lug A (S) to terminal-strip lug P-4 (DS).

- [ ] Connect tickler-winding lead AA (lead toward the adjustment screw) to P-4 (DS).

- [ ] Run a lead from P-4 (DS) to terminal-strip lug O-1 (DS).

- [ ] Connect tickler-winding lead BB to transistor-socket terminal H-1 (collector) (S). Be *careful* when connecting to transistor sockets. The tiny lugs are so close together that it is extremely easy to let a blob of solder hook two lugs together—with deplorable results later!

- [ ] Connect a lead from transistor-socket terminal H-2 (base) (S) to P-3 (DS).

- [ ] Connect one lead of capacitor S (.005 mfd) to P-3 (DS), and the other lead to lug L (DS).

- [ ] Connect resistor T (22K) between P-3 (DS) and lug L (DS).

- [ ] Connect resistor R (100K) between P-3 (S) and P-4 (S).

- [ ] Connect resistor V (1K) between lug L (DS) and P-2 (DS).

- [ ] Run a lead from lug L (DS) to variable-capacitor lug K-1 (DS).

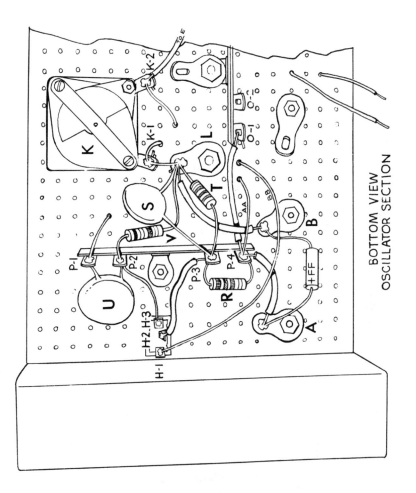

BOTTOM VIEW
OSCILLATOR SECTION

— 93 —

☐ Run a bare wire from transistor-socket terminal H-3 (S) to P-2 (DS).

☐ Connect capacitor U (.01 mfd) between P-2 (S) and P-1 (DS).

☐ Run a bare wire from P-1 (S) to terminal G-2 on tuning coil (S).

☐ Run a bare wire from coil terminal G-3 (S) to variable-capacitor lug K-1 (S).

☐ Run a lead from K-2 (DS) to antenna jack E (S).

☐ Run a bare wire from variable-capacitor lug K-2 (S) to coil terminal G-1 (S).

☐ Connect lug L (S) to lug B (S). (Use the heavy tip on your iron for lug-L connection, which requires plenty of heat.)

Look It Over Thoroughly!

Wiring done? Now is the time to check and recheck, to see that it has been done right. A mistake could cost you a transistor, so be careful.

If everything seems all right, plug in the 2N170 (or equivalent) transistor. Then plug in the antenna lead, draping it loosely over a radio, and turn the radio on.

Now hook up the batteries. Note that we are using 6-volt ones this time. You can solder four flashlight cells in series (see

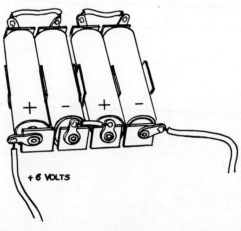

+ 6 VOLTS

"Speaker Amplifier") or use one of the battery holders shown. If using the latter, be certain the batteries are correctly placed in the holder, so that "plus" goes to clip A and "minus" to clip B. Otherwise, you won't get the six volts needed.

Turn up the volume control on your home radio, and tune to some spot near the center of the dial where you do not hear a station. Now turn the knob on the home broadcaster. If all is well, at some point—corresponding roughly to the same dial setting on the home broadcaster—you will hear the rushing sound mentioned previously. If you don't hear it, turn up the volume control more. If still no sound, tune in a station on the radio, and again adjust the knob on the home broadcaster. When the home broadcaster hits the same frequency as that of the station to which the radio is tuned, you will hear a whistle.

Chances are good, at this point, that you will get the results you want — positive indication the oscillator half of the home broadcaster circuit is working. If not, check everything again.

If everything looks all right, but the unit still will not oscillate, *reverse* the tickler-winding leads (leads AA and BB). Solder lead AA to H-1 and BB to P-4. This coil winding *must* be correctly polarized, or the set won't oscillate. If this step does not clear up the trouble, see the chapter on simple servicing techniques.

We'll assume you can pick up the oscillator loud and clear on the radio. This means you are half done! Now let's add the modulator, so we can do some broadcasting. But first, *disconnect* the battery.

Wiring the Modulator

☐ Connect the red lead from transformer X to jack lug J-1 (S).

☐ Connect the blue lead from transformer X to J-2 (S).

☐ Connect the green lead from transformer X to lug I (DS).

☐ Connect the yellow lead from transformer X to lug M (DS).

☐ Connect the red lead from transformmer D to lug M (DS).

☐ Connect the blue lead from transformer D to transistor-socket lug Q-1 (collector) (S). (The center black lead is *not* used.)

☐ Connect the yellow lead from transformer D to lug M (DS).

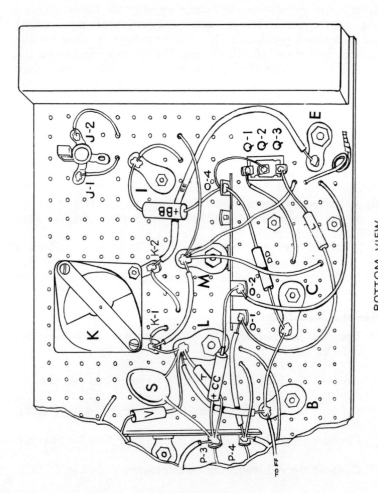

BOTTOM VIEW
MODULATOR SECTION

☐ Run a lead from lug M (S) to terminal K-1 on the variable capacitor. Be careful, when adding a new connection to K-1, not to destroy the previous solder joint.

☐ Connect resistor L (82 ohm) between lug O-1 (S) and transistor-socket lug Q-3 (emitter) (S). As mentioned, soldering to the small transistor socket lugs is a ticklish job. Use the tiplet point on your soldering iron, and be careful that no spare solder runs down and shorts out the lugs.

☐ Connect the "plus" lead of capacitor CC (2 mfd) to P-3 (S) and the other lead to O-2 (DS). Solder to P-3 *carefully* (avoid disturbing any previous connection). (Electrolytic capacitors have their "plus" ends indicated by a "plus" sign or a dot of red paint.)

☐ Connect the green lead from transformer D to O-2 (S).

☐ Run a lead from lug B (S) (careful—don't disturb the previous connection) to lug C (DS).

☐ Connect DD (270K) between lug C (S) and O-4 (DS).

☐ Run a lead from transistor-socket lug Q-2 (base) (S) to O-4 (DS).

☐ Connect the "plus" lead of capacitor BB (2 mfd) to O-4 (S) and the other lead to lug I (S).

This should complete your wiring. At this point, it is a good idea to take a red pencil and recheck the step-by-step wiring instructions, to be certain you have made no mistakes. Also check against the schematic.

Now plug in the phone (if it has a replaceable earpiece, screw on the mouthpiece) and the 2N107 (or equivalent) transistor. Connect the battery.

As before, arrange the unit near an operating radio. Again tune to a quiet spot (no station) near the center of the dial. Tune the knob on the home broadcaster until you hear the now-familiar rushing sound in the radio.

Speak into the microphone. Your voice should come out of the radio. If not loud enough, turn the radio volume control up a bit, just as you would to receive any other radio station. You may find that moving the home broadcaster dial slightly in either direction will make the voice stronger and clearer. Experiment until you get the best results.

If the set generates a terrific howl—called audio feedback—move the microphone away from the front of the speaker; or better yet, keep the microphone behind the radio. Also reducing the volume on the radio may eliminate the feedback.

· With the six-foot antenna attached to the home broadcaster, the transmitting range is quite limited, perhaps six to eight feet at the most. You can increase this range considerably—enough to reach the house next door (provided you don't live on an estate or a farm!)—by hooking the unit to a good antenna (such as the 90-foot L described previously), and connecting a ground to clip C. The latter is a good idea, anyway. It not only increases the transmitter range, but also reduces "hand capacity" effects (the detuning effect as your hand comes near the dial of the broadcaster).

To hook onto the outside antenna, simply wrap the antenna lead of the home broadcaster around the lead-in of the outside antenna, as explained in Chapter 2. (See the drawing on how to couple to a telephone line.) Make no direct connection. We want very *light* coupling to the antenna. Too much will over-

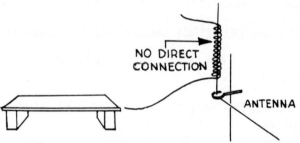

load the oscillator. As a result, it will stop oscillating, and you will hear nothing.

In addition to being used with a microphone, the home broadcaster can be utilized to play a record player through any radio. (More about that later in Chapter 12 on hi-fi and stereo.)

No, there is no switch. After you've finished, just disconnect the battery!

Actual-Sized Template

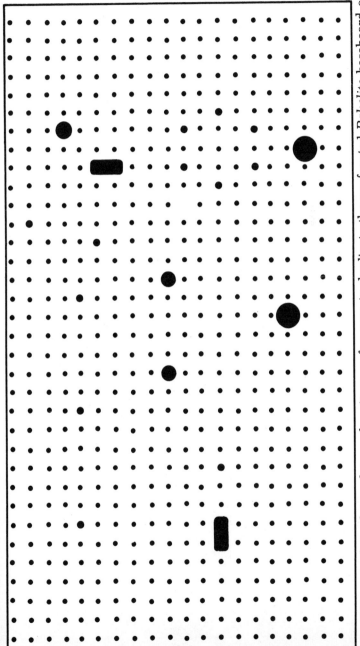

This actual-sized template makes it easy for you to duplicate the perforated *Bakelite* baseboard on which the parts are mounted. Line up the rows of small holes on the template with the holes in the *Bakelite*; then using the template as a pattern, drill and file the larger holes.

CHAPTER 10

Utility Amplifier Is a . . .

Phono Amplifier

Signal Tracer

Simple Call System

Here is a piece of equipment you will want to keep on your workbench. Although inexpensive to build, it can do a half dozen useful jobs for you.

For example, if you want a speaker output from one of the pocket sets or the short-wave receiver described in this book, the utility amplifier will do the job easily. Used with any standard high-output crystal or ceramic phonograph pickup, it will provide good-quality phono output—plenty for the average room.

By plugging a sensitive crystal microphone into the amplifier input, you can create a low-powered public-address amplifier. With it you can step up your voice a bit, perhaps for a simple call system between the house and garage.

Simply by adding a couple of test leads, you can use the amplifier for signal tracing (one of the service techniques described later), to troubleshoot not only the sets you build, but manufactured ones as well.

Furthermore, the professional metal chassis type of construction is used. Thus, you get a crack at some techniques you will use again and again as you progress in electronics.

Convinced? Let's go!

First, the Big Picture . . .

As we have learned to do, let's study the circuit diagram to see what we are about to build.

The utility amplifier is simply a 4-stage audio amplifier. If you will compare its circuit with those of the headphone and speaker amplifiers described earlier, you will see many similarities.

However, there are some differences, too. One is provision for a choice of inputs, available simply by throwing a switch. A fairly low-impedance input—ideal should you want to use the amplifier with a transistor receiver—is one of the choices.

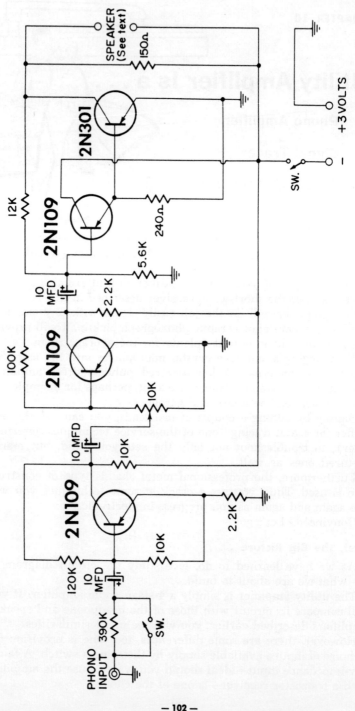

The other input circuit, in which a resistor is added in series with the input lead, supplies a fairly high impedance—perfect for a crystal-type phono pickup. In addition to the series resistor, impedance is raised by a technique known as *degeneration* (exactly the *opposite* from the regeneration in pocket sets). Although there is some sacrifice in gain, the input impedance of the first transistor is raised, and the range of frequencies handled by the amplifier is improved.

Similar feedback circuits are used throughout the amplifier. Again, some gain is sacrificed; but the ability of the unit to develop good quality is improved, so that an oboe sounds like an oboe, not like a glockenspiel!

Three of the transistors are of the general-purpose audio type used in previous equipment; the final transistor is a power audio unit. The latter, as in the speaker amplifier, feeds a speaker directly, eliminating the usual costly (and power-wasting) speaker output transformer.

Shopping List

Quantity	Description	In Drawing, Part Labeled:
1	Single-pole, single-throw switch	A
3	10-mfd, 15-volt electrolytic capacitors	C, D, E
1	120K (120,000-ohm), ½-watt resistor	CC
1	390K (390,000-ohm), ½-watt resistor	R
2	10K (10,000-ohm), ½-watt resistors	FF, H
2	2.2K (2,200-ohm), ½-watt resistors	U, V
1	10K (10,000-ohm) volume control with SPST switch	JK
1	12K (12,000-ohm), ½-watt resistor	Y
1	240-ohm, ½-watt resistor	W

Quantity	Description	In Drawing, Part Labeled:
1	150-ohm, ½-watt resistor	AA
1	100K (100,000-ohm 1 2-watt resistor	I
1	5.6K (5600-ohm) 1/2-watt resistor	O
2	Battery holders for standard flashlight cells	HH, KK
1	5"x 9½" x 2" aluminum chassis	
1	Phono input jack and plug	B
1	2-terminal screw-type terminal strip	GG
3	2N109 transistors or equivalent (2N217 or SK3004)	BB, L, X
1	2N301 power transistor (Equivalent SK3009)	Z
1	Power-transistor socket assembly, including insulating washer	
3	3-terminal transistor sokets	BB, L, X
1	Speaker—8-16 ohm. (Ohmage is extremely important. See text.)	
	Hardware—miscellaneous soldering lugs, 6-32 machine screws and nuts, etc.	

Metalworking Made Easy

Once all the parts are on hand, we're ready to start our actual building. Step one is to cut and drill the chassis.

The chassis, a 5″ × 9½″ × 2″ unit, is available from any well-stocked parts jobber. Buy an *aluminum* chassis, because it is much

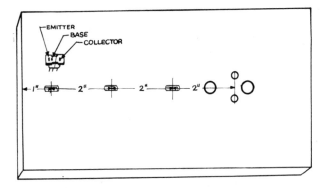

easier to work with than the steel chassis (which sells for approximately the same price).

☐ First, mount the sockets (B, L, and X) for the small transistors. Starting from one end, mount one socket one inch from the end, on a line running down the center of the chassis. Then, in two inches, mount another, and in another two inches, the third. Previous chapters have described mounting transistor sockets, and you'll find aluminum no more difficult to work with than fiber.

The special socket for the power transistor is something else again. You will want to follow the drawing carefully. The whole matter will be clearer if you understand what you are doing.

The idea is to mount the metal-case transistor to the chassis in such a way that heat from the transistor is transferred to the chassis and, at the same time, insulate the transistor from the chassis electrically. This is accomplished by having holes large

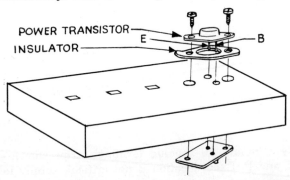

enough that both the transistor base and emitter pins *and* the transistor mounting screws clear the chassis as they are connected to the insulated socket below. The case of the transistor is the collector. The flat underside of the transistor is insulated from the chassis by an insulating washer, usually of mica or anodized aluminum. The latter is metal, so it conducts heat; strangely enough, it also is an excellent insulator. Remember that the *only* contact between any part of the transistor case and the chassis should be through an insulating washer.

This technique of mounting a power transistor is known as providing it with a "heat sink" to dissipate heat. The heat is transferred to the chassis which—being a large, metal surface—absorbs it easily.

☐ After all sockets are mounted, drill a hole in one end of the chassis for output terminal strip GG. (Use drills of the proper size, plus the ever-useful rat-tail file and a small, flat file like the one used on spark plugs.) Be certain the terminals clear the chassis.

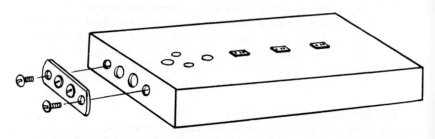

☐ On the other end, mount the single-pole, single-throw slider switch (A) and the phono input jack (B).

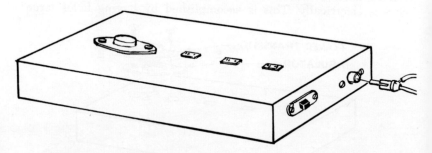

☐ Next, mount all the lug terminal strips shown—G, DD, N, and P. Exact location is not critical; simply follow the illustrations.

☐ Mount the soldering lugs, which provide for grounding to the chassis (F, H, M, and Q).

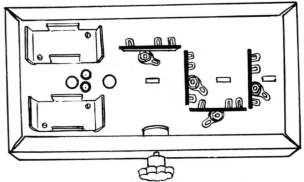

☐ Mount battery clips HH and KK. Use small bolts and nuts, and place the nuts on top of the chassis in order to leave plenty of clearance for the batteries.

☐ Mount the volume control and switch (JK) on the front of the chassis. The small transistor-type control described in previous chapters will do. If you use the larger one illustrated, follow the instructions (packed with the control) for assembling the switch on the back of the control.

Next, the wiring. This unit uses quite a few resistors and capacitors; if you are careful, their leads can serve as the wiring for many of the connections.

Wiring the First Two Stages

☐ Connect resistor R (390K) between slider switch terminals A-1 (DS) and A-2 (DS).

☐ Run a lead from switch terminal A-2 (S) to the center (insulated) phono jack terminal B-2 (S).

☐ Connect the "plus" end of capacitor C (10 mfd) to A-1 (S), and the other end to lug G-2 (DS).

☐ Run a wire from transistor socket lug BB-2 (base) (S) to terminal lug G-2 (DS).

☐ Run a lead from phono jack lug B-1 (S) to ground lug F (DS).

☐ Connect resistor U (2.2K) between ground lug F (S) and lug G-1 (DS).

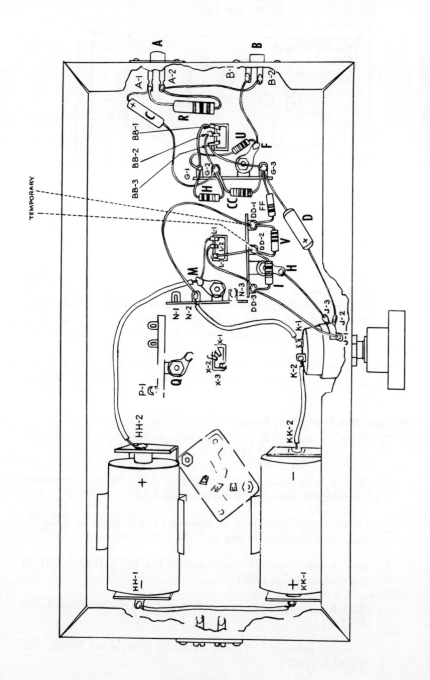

TEMPORARY

- [ ] Connect resistor H (10K) between G-1 (DS) and G-2 (DS).

- [ ] Run a lead from G-1 (S) to transistor socket lug BB-1 (emitter) (S).

- [ ] Connect resistor CC (120K) between G-2 (S) and G-3 (DS).

- [ ] Run a lead from G-3 (DS) to transistor socket terminal lug BB-3 (collector) (S).

- [ ] Connect the "plus" end of capacitor D (10 mfd) to volume-control terminal J-2 (S), and the other end to G-3 (DS).

- [ ] Connect resistor FF (10K) between G-3 (S) and terminal lug DD-1 (DS).

- [ ] Connect a temporary one-foot wire lead to DD-1 (DS).

- [ ] Connect resistor V (2.2K) between DD-1 (DS) and DD-2 (DS).

- [ ] Run a lead from DD-1 (S) to terminal lug N-2 (DS).

- [ ] Connect resistor I (100K) between DD-2 (DS) and DD-3 (DS).

- [ ] Run a lead from DD-2 (DS) to transistor socket lug L-3 (collector) (S).

- [ ] Connect a temporary one-foot lead to lug DD-2 (S).

- [ ] Run a lead from DD-3 (DS) to transistor socket lug L-2 (base) (S).

- [ ] Run a lead from DD-3 (S) to volume-control terminal J-1 (S).

- [ ] Run a lead from J-3 (S) to grounding lug H (S).

- [ ] Run a lead from transistor socket lug L-1 (emitter) (S) to grounding lug M (DS).

- [ ] Run a lead from lug M (S) to battery-clip terminal HH-2 (S).

☐ Run a lead from battery-clip terminal HH-1 (S) to terminal KK-1 (S).

☐ Connect a lead between battery lug KK-2 (S) and switch terminal K-2 (S).

☐ Run a lead from K-1 (S) to lug N-2 (S).

This should complete the wiring of the first two stages of the amplifier. Check and recheck the wiring, going over every lead on the drawing and remarking with a colored pencil.

If everything is all right, plug in the batteries (being careful to observe the polarity) and the two transistors. Be certain each transistor lead is identified and inserted in the proper hole.

Signal Generator Quick and Easy

Now we need a signal to feed into our amplifier. An easy way to get one is to utilize the *One Hour* radio, as shown in the photo-

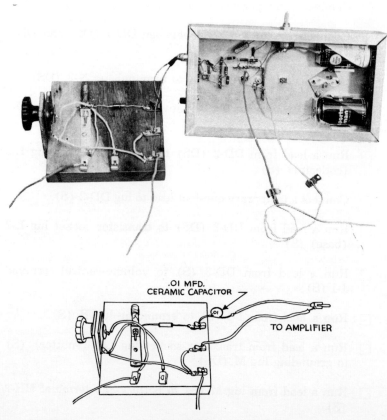

.01 MFD.
CERAMIC CAPACITOR

TO AMPLIFIER

graph. To do this, hook up a phono plug with two leads, which can be connected to the headphone output of the *One Hour* radio (see sketch). You could hook up the leads directly; but for better tonal quality, it is better to connect a .01-mfd ceramic capacitor in series with the lead going to the terminal on the *One Hour* radio.

Tune in the crystal set in the usual way, first checking (with the crystal earphone) across the set terminals to make certain a signal is present. If everything is satisfactory, connect the headphone to the temporary headphone leads (connected to DD-1 and DD-2) on the amplifier.

Snap on the amplifier, and turn up the volume control. You should hear the crystal set, and the volume control should vary the output. Don't expect any great volume—the gain is low, particularly in the first stage. The important point is that you hear the signal at all. If so, you are ready to go on to the next two stages. If not, read the chapter on servicing; then start tracking down the trouble.

Adding the Speaker Stages

We're ready to wire again!

☐ Clip off the temporary leads used for the headphone.

☐ Connect the "plus" lead of capacitor E (10 mfd) to N-3 (DS), and the other lead to DD-2 (S), being careful not to disturb any previous connections.

☐ Connect resistor O (5.6K) between N-3 (DS) and grounding lug Q (DS).

☐ Run a lead from N-3 (DS) to transistor socket lug X-2 (S).

☐ Connect resistor Y (12K) between N-3 (S) and transistor socket lug Z-2 (collector) (DS).

☐ Run a lead from Z-2 (S) to GG-1 (DS).

☐ Connect resistor AA (150 ohms) between GG-1 (S) and GG-2 (DS).

☐ Run a lead from GG-2 (S) to K-1 (DS).

☐ Connect a lead from K-1 (S) to transistor socket lug X-3 (S).

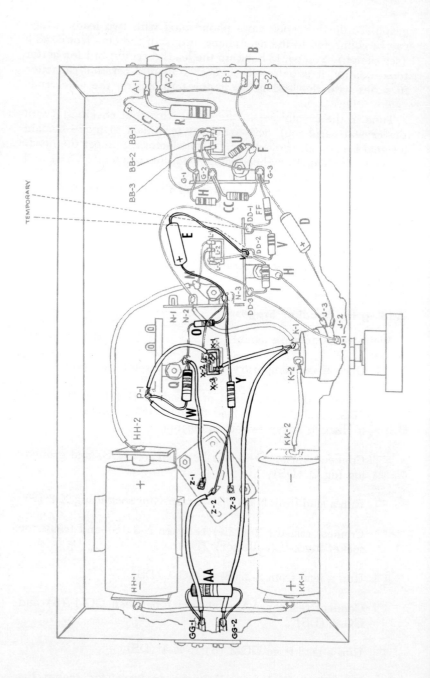

☐ Run a lead from X-1 (S) to P-1 (DS).

☐ Run a lead from P-1 (DS) to Z-3 (base) (S).

☐ Connect resistor W (240 ohms) between P-1 (S) and grounding lug Q (DS).

☐ Run a lead from lug Q (S) to transistor socket lug Z-1 (emitter) (S).

Putting the Amplifier to Work

Now plug in the power transistor. Make *certain* (using one of the techniques in the chapter on servicing) there is *no* connection between the metal case of the power transistor and the chassis.

We're ready to try out the amplifier. The ideal speaker for it is an extended-range, 16-ohm speaker, 8 inches or larger. (In the chapter on hi-fi, we'll learn more about speakers of this type.) However, we can use a smaller, 8-ohm transistor speaker—in fact, the same speaker used for the speaker amplifier described earlier. *Under no circumstance should the speaker have an impedance lower than 8 ohms;* 16 ohms will give *much* better results.

Once you have selected a proper speaker, connect it to the output terminals. To the input terminals, of course, connect whatever you want to amplify.

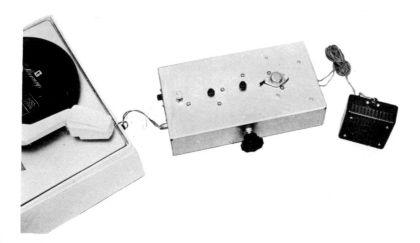

Let's assume you want to use the unit as a phono amplifier for a record player. Simply connect the phono lead from the phono pickup (which should be of high-impedance crystal or ceramic, and fairly high in output) to the amplifier input. Ordinarily, the lead from a record player will have a phono plug which fits the jack on the unit.

Turn on the amplifier, and start the record player. Barring any trouble, you should hear the record player in the speaker, and the volume will be satisfactory. (Try the slide switch both ways—one way gives better quality.) The volume control on the amplifier controls the output, of course.

To use the unit as a voice amplifier, simply plug a high-output crystal microphone (the type used with tape recorders is satisfactory) into the input plug, and talk into the microphone. Keep the microphone *behind* the speaker. Otherwise, you are apt to get an ear-splitting howl known as audio feedback!

Since the amplifier is battery operated, it is ideal for use outdoors, with a battery-operated turntable and pickup. You may want to fit the amplifier, speaker, and record player into a nice-looking case.

The uses mentioned for the utility amplifier by no means exhaust its possibilities. We'll learn of some others later.

CHAPTER 11

Short Wave Receiver

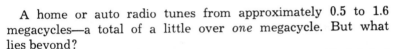

Tunes the World

A home or auto radio tunes from approximately 0.5 to 1.6 megacycles—a total of a little over *one* megacycle. But what lies beyond?

The answer is . . . *plenty!* Within the spectrum usually labeled *short wave* or *high frequency* there are many, many thousands of stations operating, day and night. And within this range, particularly from 6 megacycles on up, it is no trick at all to pick up foreign stations direct. Doing so can be a lot of fun—particularly if you work at it by writing to the stations you hear, and asking for one of their verification cards. Many of them will send you cards, and serious SWL's (as short wave listeners are called) often have their rooms plastered with cards from all over the world.

Because of the high frequencies involved, building a short wave receiver is a bit more difficult than is the case with a broadcast band set. Also, because signals are weaker, the set must be more complicated in order to provide the extra amplification needed.

The simplest type of short wave set consists of a regenerative detector, plus some audio amplifier stages. A detector circuit like that shown in Chapter 8 will work after a fashion. However, to do the job right, we have to use a somewhat more complex circuit, and a different type of transistor, called an FET (field-effect transistor).

This transistor has the tremendous advantage of having a very high input impedance, which in practical terms means that it can be used with a tuning coil without tapping the coil. The latter method works, of course, but creates building complications, and also prevents the stage from being as efficient as you would like. With the FET, however, all of the problems disappear—the transistor is no harder to use than a tube, and requires fewer parts and a lot less power.

The Integrated Circuit

Using the FET helps with the detector problems—and utilizing another new development, the integrated circuit, simplifies the rest of the set. Integrated circuits come in many, many different forms—so many that it is difficult to describe one. Perhaps it is sufficient to say that an integrated circuit is a combination of transistors, diodes, and frequently resistors and condensers—all in a single unit no larger than an ordinary transistor. As an example, the RCA 3020 integrated circuit which is used in the short wave set to be described contains seven transistors and two diodes!

All of this means that by using integrated circuits the design and building of equipment can be greatly simplified. The one integrated circuit provides enough audio output to drive a loudspeaker when fed by a detector.

A Stage at a Time

When you look at the photographs of the short wave set, it will probably appear a bit complicated, and compared with some of the other sets in this book it actually is fairly complex. However, the design is such that the set can be built in two units, and each unit made to work by itself. This greatly reduces the chance of error, since any trouble that develops is isolated to a fixed area.

Extra care was taken in the design of the set to try to eliminate the most common trouble spots for the beginner. For example, wiring up a band-switching device, or even making up a set of plug-in coils, frequently leads the beginner astray. But this set uses only one coil, easily handmade, plus a fairly large tuning condenser, to give a good slice of the short wave spectrum. The set illustrated tunes from approximately 3.9 megacycles to 14 megacycles. Within this range are found portions of three radio amateur bands, most broadcasting stations, some aircraft stations—in fact, the bulk of what goes on in the short wave bands.

Despite its simplicity, the set will do two things which are impossible with the usual small commercial transistor radio that has a short wave band on it. First of all, it will receive amateur CW (code) stations, which means that it is ideal for code practice for the user who hopes to become a "ham." Second, with careful tuning, it will pull in the SSB amateur radiophone stations, which cannot be unscrambled at all with a short wave set unless it has either a BFO or, like this one, a regenerative detector.

Two Units

The detector stage of the set is built up in much the same fashion as the utility amplifier, with the various parts mounted either on terminal lugs or on the metal chassis itself. The amplifier stage

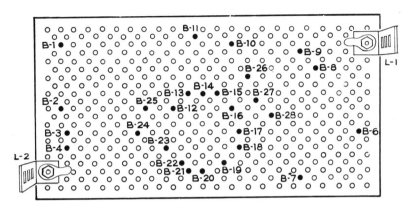

utilizes a small perforated board fitted out with "push-in" terminals (also called "flea clips"). The clips provide a practical way to mount the parts on one side of the board and the wiring on the other. By following the drawings carefully, you can come close to duplicating the layout of the original set. The board chosen has .062 (1/16″) hole size and is of the "G" or alternate grid pattern. The regular pattern board, of course, can be used instead with minor changes in layout.

The Integrated Circuit Amplifier

For building purposes this is the ideal starting point, since the amplifier will function nicely by itself, without the rest of the set being hooked onto it.

Shopping List

Quantity	Description	In Drawing Part Labeled:
1	1-mfd 15-volts electrolytic	C-1
1	1-mfd 15-volts electrolytic	C-2
1	.01-mfd ceramic capacitor	C-3
1	.1-mfd ceramic capacitor	C-4
1	1-mfd 15-volts electrolytic	C-5
1	.82-ohm 1/2-watt resistor	R-1
1	510K 1/2-watt resistor	R-2
1	500-ohm C. T.-3.2-ohm output transistor transformer	T

Quantity	Description	*In Drawing* Part Labeled:
1	RCA CA3020 integrated circuit	Int.
2	Small aluminum angles	
1	2-1/2″ speaker 3.2 ohm-V.C.	Spk.
1	Alternate hole punched plastic board 2-3/8″ x 4-3/4″	
25	Mounting clips	
2	1/4″-6/32 bolts and nuts	
4	Soldering lugs	
Misc.	Hook-up wire and speaker extension wire	

As mentioned earlier, the integrated circuit amplifier utilizes a perforated phenolic board, both parts and wiring being mounted on small "push in" terminals which mount on the perf board.

One of the drawings shows an easy way to put the terminals into the board: by using a 1-watt resistor as "pusher." The resistor has one lead clipped short, so that it is just long enough to fit down in the twin-sided end of the terminal.

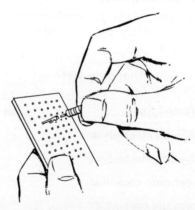

The first step in building the unit is to mount the terminal clips on the board, following the drawing which shows the layout. Note that each hole into which a clip is mounted is indicated. Try to duplicate the original layout as closely as possible. While this may appear a bit tough at first, it is not too difficult if you push the clips in one at a time, and count the holes to determine the proper locations.

Once you get the clips in place, check your work carefully. It is important that the clips are where you want them—otherwise you may make a mistake later in the wiring.

Before starting the wiring, mount the small aluminum angles as shown with 6/32 bolts and nuts, and place a soldering lug on each side of the perf board. These lugs serve as grounding points for the circuit. The metal angles, when mounted on the metal

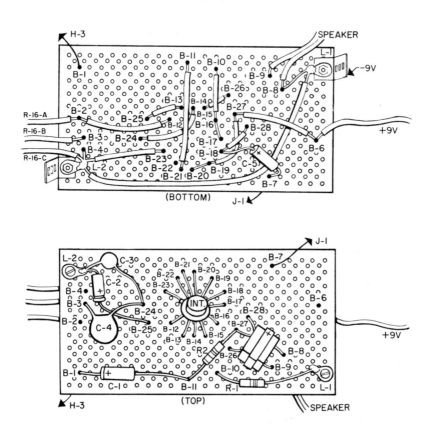

chassis, connect the perf board circuit to the rest of the wiring. The angles are made from small scraps of aluminum. One readily available source for such aluminum is a small cookie sheet.

Parts Layout

The wiring goes very fast, since you can do it without having any parts in the way. A logical sequence will help you avoid errors.

- [ ] Run a lead from L-1 (DS) to L-2 (DS).
- [ ] Connect L-2 (DS) to B-23 (S).
- [ ] Connect L-2 (DS) to B-4 (S).
- [ ] Hook lead to B-2 (S), and run to B-12 (S).
- [ ] Connect B-25 (S) to B-13 (S).
- [ ] Solder lead to B-24. Connect other end to B-14 (S).
- [ ] From B-21 runa a lead (S) to B-11 (S).
- [ ] From B-15 (S) connect a lead to B-26 (S).
- [ ] Solder lead to B-10. Connect other end to B-16 (DS).
- [ ] From B-16 (S) run short, bare lead to B-17 (S).
- [ ] With bare lead connect B-20 (S) to B-19 (DS).
- [ ] Connect lead to B-19 (S). Run to B-27 (DS).
- [ ] From B-27, connect a lead (S) and run to B-6 (DS).
- [ ] Connect lead from B-18 (DS) to B-28 (S).
- [ ] From B-8, run a lead (DS) to L-1 (S).
- [ ] Connect one lead of two-wire lead to B-8 (S).
- [ ] Solder other lead of the pair to B-9 (S).
- [ ] Connect three leads (S) to B-2, B-3, B-4. Leave each lead 6 inches long.
- [ ] Connect "plus" end of capacitor C-5 to B-18 (S).
- [ ] Connect "minus" end to B-7 (S).
- [ ] Solder a lead to B-6. Leave lead 6 inches long.

This completes the wiring underneath the board.

Turn the board over. You will probably find that solder has run down in some of the clips and plugged the mounting holes needed for mounting parts. With the board in the upright position, carefully heat lugs with iron so that solder drops down and the mounting holes open up.

Examine *all* of the clips from the underside again to be certain no connections have come loose in the process of cleaning out the mounting holes.

- [ ] Hook capacitor C-3 (.01-mfd ceramic 100 v.) to L-2 (DS).
- [ ] Connect other end of C-3 to B-24 (DS).
- [ ] Hook "minus" end of C-2 (1 mfd 15 volts) to L-2 (S).
- [ ] Connect "plus" end of C-2 to B-25 (S).
- [ ] Connect one end of C-4 (.1 mfd 100 V.) to B-3 (S).
- [ ] Connect the other end of C-4 to B-24 (S).
- [ ] Hook "plus" end of 1-mfd 15-volt C-1 to B-1 (S).
- [ ] Connect "minus" end of C-1 to B-11 (DS).
- [ ] From B-11 (S) connect 510K resistor R-2 to B-27 (DS).
- [ ] Solder one end of .82 ohm (or 1 ohm) resistor R-1 to B-10.
- [ ] Solder other end of resistor R-1 to lug L-1.

The transformer "T" is of the miniature imported type and matches 500 ohms, center-tapped, to a 3.2-ohm output, which connects to a speaker. Transformers of this type vary somewhat in construction—some, for example, must be mounted with nuts and bolts. The one shown came with stiff wire leads which were easy to solder to the terminals provided. Ordinarily, such transformers come equipped with a diagram which shows the lead layout. You need to identify the center tap of the "primary" winding. This lead connects to B-27 (S).

- [ ] The other two primary leads go to B-26 and B-28 (S).
- [ ] The 3.2-ohm secondary winding (speaker output) goes to B-8 and B-9 (S).

Once again, examine the leads from the underside to see if any wires have come loose.

The Integrated Circuit

We have saved this part for last because the soldering requires a gentle touch. *Use a heat sink on each lead as it is being soldered.* (See Chapter 13 regarding use of a heat sink.)

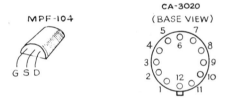

First of all, we must identify the leads. See the diagram that shows arrangement. Note that a small lug on the case of the integrated circuit shell identifies lead No. 12. This lead goes to B-23, and grounds to lug L-2 on the perf board. After you have made absolutely certain which lead is No. 12—fan out the leads as shown in the drawing. *If* you have the first lead correct, the rest will all be correct, providing the lug arrangement is as shown.

Solder the leads one at a time—*protecting the integrated circuit with a heat sink.* Use a small iron, and as little heat as necessary to make good connections. Solder a lead—then move the heat sink to the next lead, solder it, etc. Wiring in the integrated circuit completes the board itself. At this point, do a very careful rechecking job of the wiring, to make certain that you have made no errors. Examine *each* soldered connection, preferably with a reading glass and by pulling and tugging on the wire or part.

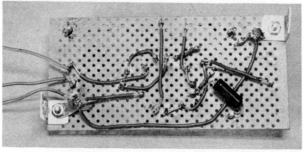

Kit makers have learned that bad soldering is the most common cause of problems with home-built equipment. In fact, when a non-functioning kit is sent to the kit manufacturer for repair—unless standard service procedures isolate the trouble quickly, it is a frequent practice for the service technician to go through and resolder every connection in the unit under test.

Testing the Integrated Circuit Amplifiers

The amplifier is complete in itself, all we need to do is to add a speaker, apply voltage, hook up the volume control, and furnish a test signal. First, solder the speaker leads to the voice coil terminals on the speaker.

Now—connect some sort of audio signal. This can be a small transistorized signal injector—or the "One Hour Radio," used as a signal source, as was described in Chapter 10 and shown in the photograph. Note that the lead that comes from the diode of the little radio connects to terminal B-1 on the integrated circuit perf board. The "ground" side of the radio goes to lug L-1.

We are now all set to go—except for adding the battery. For this we need 9 volts. A small 9-volt transistor radio battery will operate the amplifier, but the current drain is fairly high, and battery life will be short. A far better idea is to make a 9-volt battery out of standard "D" section flashlight cells. The batteries are connected in series exactly as was illustrated in Chapter 5. *Each* cell yields 1.5 volts, so we will need six. Connect them in "series"—plus to minus—plus to minus—plus to minus, etc.—so that you wind up with one which is the "minus" end (the case of the cell) and one which is the "plus" (the center pole end). Do a good soldering job—a high resistance contact at this point can cause all kinds of trouble. A 100-watt iron—a soldering gun—is best for this task because the metal case of the battery tends to drain the heat away. If you must use a small iron, scrape the metal surfaces on the batteries before soldering, and work quickly.

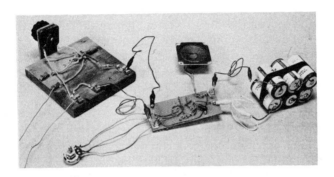

The photo shows a completed 9-volt battery. Such a battery will give hundreds of hours of life in the short-wave set.

Note that the "plus" end of the battery connects to terminal B-6 —the "minus" end to the metal angle that serves as the ground point for L-2. *Do not make a mistake at this point.* If the polarity of the battery is *reversed* the integrated circuit may be *destroyed instantly.*

Assuming that you have the One-Hour Radio tuned to a station, the minute you hook up the battery, the amplifier should come on and operate the speaker. If there is good, strong headphone vol-

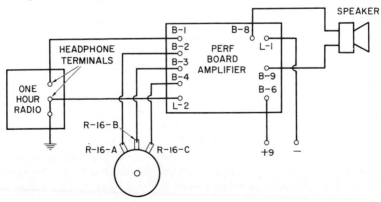

ume provided from the set, you will probably have to turn down the volume control—the amplifier has more than enough gain to drive a speaker from the output of the diode detector.

If you hear nothing, turn the amplifier off *immediately*. Check and re-check your wiring. Be certain that you identified the leads properly in hooking up the integrated circuit. Check soldering. Check the wiring against the circuit diagram, as well as the pictorial—this will often reveal an error. Finally, read the chapter on servicing which offers some additional suggestions.

The perf board method of wiring is so easy to follow that chances are good that you won't make a mistake—and the amplifier will come on the minute you apply power. You will discover that it is an excellent unit—easily the equivalent in output of the amplifier stages described in Chapter 4 and Chapter 5 combined. The former, however, for the real beginner, has the advantage of being easier to build, thanks to the very simple design and breadboard layout.

The Short Wave Detector

Once your amplifier unit is working properly, the next step is to build the tuner. Before you tackle this, it is a good idea to have some understanding of what you are building.

As you may know if you have built other sets, the sensitivity of a detector can be increased a great deal by the process of "regeneration." Since short-wave signals are much weaker than broadcast band signals, we need all of the help we can get, so this detector is made regenerative.

The FET (field-effect transistor) chosen for the detector works much better than older transistors. However, it is important to use the transistor specified. If you cannot locate one locally, write to the manufacturer for the name of a nearby supplier.

The detector unit is built up on a 3x5x7-inch metal chassis. Everything except the FET itself goes inside the chassis. This method of construction is a bit more difficult than that of stringing parts along the topside of the chassis, but for the short-wave set of this type it offers some real advantages: shielding of the coil and tuning capacitor; shielding of the wiring from stray hum pickup; and a good, solid "panel" to eliminate movement of parts associated with the tuning capacitor, an important consideration for the stability needed to tune in elusive SSB phone stations.

The set also has a couple of other luxuries, both of which in the writer's opinion are well worth the modest extra trouble and expense. The tuning system uses two variable capacitors in parallel. This provides what is called electrical bandspread—a very small band of frequencies is spread over the complete tuning range of the smaller of the two variable capacitors. This makes it easy to tune in the short wave stations—which can be extremely sharp tuning on a set without bandspread. In addition, two regeneration controls are provided, one "coarse" and the other "fine." Again, this makes for easy tuning.

Like any simple regenerative short-wave set, this one takes some tuning skill to achieve good results. However, the design has helped remove some of the difficulties, and with an hour or two of practice you should be able to pick up foreign stations with ease.

Shopping List

Quantity	Description	In Drawing Part Labeled:
1	365-picofarad (mmf) miniature variable capacitor, single gang	C-6
1	2.9-16.9-picofarad (mmf) variable capacitor (any small variable with 15-picofarad to 25-picofarad maximum capacity)	C-7
1	50-picofarad (mmf) silver mica fixed capacitor	C-8
1	.033-mfd (or .02 mfd) 100-volt (or higher) ceramic capacitor	C-9
1	270-picofarad (mmf) mica capacitor, 100 volts or higher	C-10
1	.001-mfd. (1000-mmf) ceramic 100 volts or higher	C-11
1	100-mfd. 25 volt electrolytic	C-12
1	365-picofarad (mmf) subminiature wafer-type variable capacitor	C-13
1	Midget transistor audio input transformer. Primary 200 K (secondary unused). See text.	T-2
1	1-megohm 1/2-watt resistor	R-3
1	2.5-Mh R-F choke	RFC
1	Ph-1 RCA-type phono input jack	PH-1

Quantity	Description	In Drawing Part Labeled:
1	Subminiature phone jack (preferably open circuit type) for headphone	J-1
1	Fahenstock clip	CL
1	0-5000-ohm (5K) variable resistor (volume control) linear taper	(RG-1, 2, 3)
1	0-100,000-ohm (100K) variable resistor (volume control) linear taper spst switch	RG-4-5-6)
1	5000-ohm volume control	R16
1	Socket for transistor 3-hole, preferably "in line" type	SKT
3	Knobs	
1	Pointer knob	
1	2″ vernier dial	
1	1-1/2″ vernier dial	
1	Coil (See text)	L-1, L-2, L-3
1	Roll No. 20 solid hook-up wire plastic insulation	
1	Aluminum bracket (See text)	
4	Terminal strips (See text)	G, H, M, N
1	Rubber grommet for 1/4″ hole	
6	"D" size flashlight batteries	
Misc.	6/32 nuts and bolts and other mounting hardware	
1	Crystal earphone	

Mounting Parts

As the first step, cut the speaker hole, which should be about 1-1/4″ in diameter. A socket punch is ideal for the purpose, but if you do not have one, drill the largest hole you can, and finish it off with a rattail file. Using the speaker as a template, mark the four holes needed for mounting it. Glue a piece of grill cloth, which can be any loosely-woven cloth, over the hole. Do *not* mount the speaker until the other parts are all in—it is too easy to have a tool slip and punch a hole in the speaker cone!

Exactly where the front panel parts should be mounted depends on the exact shape of the parts chosen. Assuming that you are using identical parts with the original, the first step is to determine the location for C-6, the 365-picofarad (365 mmf) capacitor used for band-setting. It is mounted against one end of the chassis. Hold

the capacitor in place, and determine where the shaft hits the front panel of the chassis. For the sake of appearance, the shaft should be centered vertically on the panel—which means that it should be 1-1/2″ from the bottom.

- [ ] Drill a large hole (at least 1/2″) to allow the vernier dial shaft to protrude. (See the photo.) Hold the vernier dial in place, and determine placement of mounting holes for it, and make certain the shaft will rotate without binding. Then mount the capacitor to the chassis with a suitable bolt. Be careful to use one short enough so that it secures the capacitor without shorting the stationary plates of the capacitor to ground.
- [ ] Next, fabricate a small aluminum angle for the small tuning capacitor C7. Again, try to have the shaft 1-1/2″ from the bottom of the chassis, so that the larger vernier dial is centered on the front of the chassis.
- [ ] Mount the angle to the chassis with a nut and bolt. Mount the vernier dial.
- [ ] Drill a 3/8″ hole and mount the "fine" regeneration control

(RG-1, 2, 3). For sake of appearance, it should be mounted the same distance from the end of the chassis as was C-6.

☐ The "coarse" regeneration control (RG-4, 5, 6) is mounted on the end of the chassis, as close as possible to (RG-1, 2, 3).

☐ Mount the transistor socket on the chassis. Different sockets have different mounting arrangements—use whichever is needed for yours.

☐ On the back of the chassis, mount the terminal strip, G, which should have one lug that grounds to the chassis and three insulated lugs.

☐ In a 1/4″ hole, mount the headphone jack J-1.

☐ Mount the RCA-type phono jack PH-1.

☐ Mount the midget variable capacitor C-13.

☐ Bolt the lid of the 1-1/4″ plastic pill box (which serves as a coil form) to the end of the chassis.

☐ Mount the volume control, R-16.

☐ Bolt terminal strip H to the chassis. This terminal strip should have two insulated lugs and one grounded lug.

☐ Mount terminal strip M to the chassis. This terminal strip should have one grounded lug and three insulated lugs.

☐ Mount terminal strip L. This terminal strip should have one grounded lug and three insulated lugs.

☐ Following the drawing, mount the input transformer on a terminal strip, and then bolt the strip to the chassis.

☐ In a 1/4″ hole in the rear of the chassis, push in a rubber grommet.

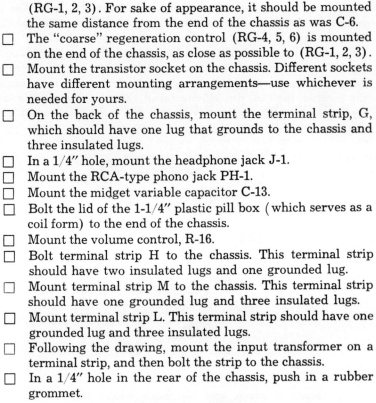

This completes mounting all of the parts, with the exception of the grounding clip at the rear of the chassis, which is simply bolted to the chassis.

Starting the Assembly

- [ ] Using two-wire speaker extension wire, make up a battery-supply lead. Ordinarily this wire is "polarized"—one lead is silver-colored and the other copper-colored. Run the wire through the grommet and tie a knot about 3 inches from the end inside the chassis.
- [ ] The *copper*-colored lead is the "plus" and goes to terminal G-2 (DS).
- [ ] The *silver*-colored lead is the "minus" and goes to terminal G-3, which is grounded to the chassis (DS).
- [ ] From G-3, run "minus" end of 100-mfd capacitor C-12 (S) to terminal G-1 (DS).
- [ ] Remove the phono jack-Ph-1, temporarily, to allow room to install the perf board amplifier.
- [ ] Mount the speaker, placing a soldering lug under the top left bolt of the four bolts mounting the speaker (looking at speaker from rear.)
- [ ] Connect the speaker to the perf board amplifier by means of two-wire speaker lead. Solder all four connections. (Two on perf board, two on speaker.)
- [ ] Mount the perf board vertically, bolting the brackets to the chassis. Bolt down *hard*—the brackets carry the "minus" to the perf board from the chassis.
- [ ] Run a lead B-7 (S) to lug on headphone jack J-1. Examine this jack closely. Ignore the lug which grounds to the chassis. Solder lead to the lug which is insulated from the chassis and connects to the tip of the crystal earphone input plug.
- [ ] Connect a two-wire lead (polarity unimportant) to SW-1 and SW-2 on regeneration control (S).
- [ ] Connect the other end to G-1 (DS) and G-2 (S).
- [ ] From G-1, (S), run a lead to B-6 (S).
- [ ] Wire the three-wire leads which connect R-16-A, R-16-B, and R-16-C to B-2, B-3, B-4. Be certain that the right lug on the volume control connects to the proper terminal on the perf board (S).
- [ ] Solder a lead to B-6 on perf board. Run other end to terminal lug G-1 (S).

At this point, we have the perf board amplifier installed in the chassis and ready to go. Check over the connections—be *certain* that the "plus" lead from the battery goes to G-2. The switch, of course, when turned on feeds the "plus" to G-1—which in turn goes to B-6 on the perf board.

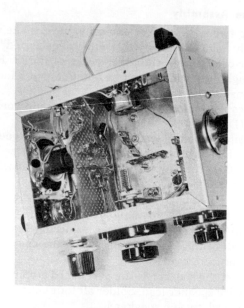

Hook up the battery. Remember that by our code system the "minus" goes to the silver lead which grounds to the chassis. Turn on switch, and advance the volume control. With your finger on the metal shaft of a screwdriver, touch terminal B-1. You should hear a hum (caused by pick-up from your body). Varying the volume control should increase and decrease the strength of the hum.

Of course, instead of the crude form of signal injection described, you can use a signal from the One-Hour Radio, or from a transistorized signal injector or other audio signal generator. Amplifier okay? Fine—now we'll wire the detector. But first, we must make a coil.

Winding the Coil

Our coil form is a plastic pill box, which measures 1-1/4" in diameter, and 2-3/4" long. The form is wound with regular No. 20

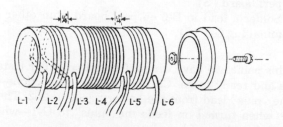

L-1   L-2   L-3 L-4   L-5   L-6

hook-up wire, used for wiring much of the set. The use of the fairly large wire improves the "Q" of the circuit (aiding selectivity) and has the added advantage of making it unnecessary to buy another size of wire for the coil alone.

Note that there is a four-turn antenna coil (L-1, L-2), a 12-turn tuning coil, (L-3, L-4) and five-turn ticker coil (L-5, L-6.) Follow the drawing in winding the coil. *Note that all windings are made in the same direction.* Note, also, that the wire leads are pulled across inside the coil form to ensure that the winding is "locked" fairly tightly. Try to keep the windings tight and smooth. A few dabs of household cement will help in holding the wires in place.

Wiring the Detector

We will start by wiring in the regeneration controls. Clean your soldering iron, good soldered joints are extremely important in a detector circuit.

- ☐ From the "Source" (S) connection on the transistor socket (S), run a lead to lug M-3 (DS).
- ☐ Connect a lead to M-3 (DS) and run it to RG-1 (S).
- ☐ Run a lead from RG-2 (S) to RG-3 (DS).
- ☐ From RG-3 (S) run a lead to RG-4 (S).
- ☐ Connect RG-5 and RG-6 together (S) and run a lead to the grounding lug mounted on the speaker (S).
- ☐ Solder one end of C-9 (.033-mfd or 0.2 mfd) to M-3.
- ☐ Solder other end to M-2. This lug grounds to chassis—the other three on "M" should be insulated from ground.
- ☐ From "Gate" (G) connection on the transistor socket (S) run a short lead to terminal lug N-1 (DS).
- ☐ Hook 1-megohm 1/2-watt resistor R-3 to N-1 (DS).
- ☐ Solder the other end of R-3 to N-2, the grounded lug on terminal strip N.
- ☐ Hook one end 50-picofarad (mmf) silver mica capacitor C-8 to N-1 (S).
- ☐ Connect other end to N-4 (DS).
- ☐ From N-4 (S) run shortest possible lead to C-7-B (DS). C-7-B is the stationary plate connection on the variable capacitor.
- ☐ Connect a lead to C-7-B (S) and run it to the stationary plate connection of C-6 (C-6-B) (S).
- ☐ From C-7-A, run a lead (DS) to C-6-A (S).
- ☐ Connect a lead to "D" terminal on transistor socket (S).
- ☐ Connect other end of the lead to lug N-3 (DS).
- ☐ Connect 2.5 mh R-F choke to M-4 (DS).
- ☐ Hook other end of the choke to M-1 (DS).

- [ ] Connect 270-picofarad (mmf) mica capacitor (C10) to M-4 (DS).
- [ ] Run other end of C10 to lug H-2 (DS) (grounded lug).
- [ ] Hook capacitor C-11 to H-2 (S) and connect other end to lug M-1 (DS).
- [ ] Connect a lead to M-1 (S) and run to H-3 (DS).
- [ ] Connect a lead to H-3 (DS) and run to B-1 on perf board (S).
- [ ] Run lead from G-1 (S) to lug H-1 (DS).
- [ ] Hook red lead from transformer T-2 (200K ohm primary) to H-1 (S).
- [ ] Connect green lead from transformer T-2 (the second of the two leads for the primary winding) to lug H-3 (S).

This completes the wiring, except for adding the coil. This hides the parts below it, so now is the time to check over the wiring

carefully. A high-resistance soldered joint in a detector circuit invariably means that it won't work. So inspect all soldered joints. Be particularly careful with connections to terminal lugs to which several wires are attached. It is all too easy to have one wire connect but another only seem to connect.

Hooking Up the Coil

Identify the coil leads as shown in the drawing.

- [ ] Solder L-2 to C-13 A. This is the *stationary plate* terminal on the sub-miniature 365-picofarad (mmf) variable capacitor.
- [ ] Push the coil onto the lid which serves as the mounting base.

- [ ] Connect L-6 to N-3 (S).
- [ ] Connect L-5 to M-4 (S).
- [ ] Hook L-4 to C-7-A (S).
- [ ] Wire L-3 to C-7-B (S).
- [ ] Hook L-1 to center terminal PH-1.

This completes the wiring. We're now ready to try out our handiwork!

Controls

Tuning a short-wave receiver, especially a regenerative set, is definitely an art. And unless you learn it, you will be disappointed in the performance of the set.

First, let's review what the controls are for. The control on the left end, looking at the set from the front, is the volume control. This works exactly like the control on a radio or TV set.

The small vernier dial to the left controls the "band setting" tuning capacitor. This capacitor covers the whole tuning range—but because it is quite large for short wave bands (the penalty for requiring only one coil instead of plug-in coils or complicated band switching) means that the tuning, using this capacitor, is extremely sharp and critical.

The large vernier dial is the actual tuning capacitor. It has only about one twentieth of the capacity of the larger capacitor, which means that it tunes about one twentieth as sharp. On this capacitor, shore-wave stations tune much the same as would be the case with the tuning capacitor with a standard radio. The knob at the right controls regeneration—and like the small tuning capacitor, is non-critical in adjustment. The knob on the end of the chassis

sets the "range" within which the front panel control operates, and is a bit critical in adjustment.

Most tuning is done with the center vernier dial and the knob immediately to the right. On the rear of the chassis is the variable capacitor in series with the antenna. This allows adjustment to the antenna in use, and requires little adjustment once it has been set to the proper spot.

The Actual Tuning

For our first effort, let's try the set in the late afternoon or early evening. At this time the foreign and domestic short-wave broadcast stations start to come in, and the signal strength usually builds up until at least 10 p.m.

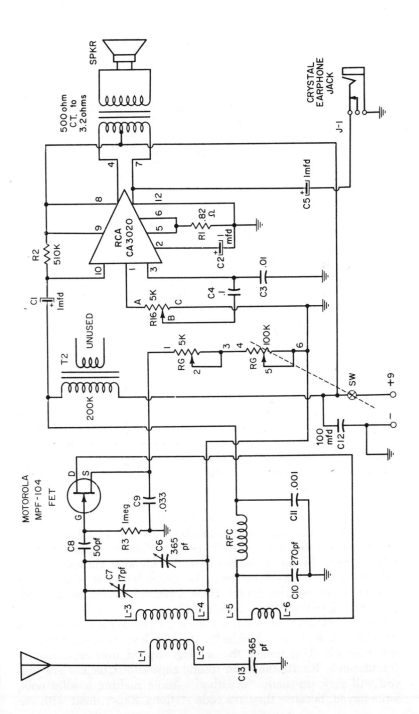

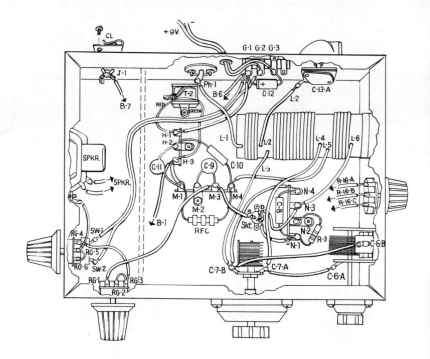

Set the antenna tuning capacitor open as far as it will go. Set the band setting capacitor about half open—or about "50" on the dial. Turn the volume control fully on—then back it off a little. Set the front panel regeneration control at about half open.

Rotate the regeneration control on the end of the chassis in the maximum counter-clockwise position.

Hook on the antenna—ideally this should be an outside antenna, at least 50 feet long. See an earlier chapter on building the antenna. The set will work with about 20 feet of flexible wire strung around the room—but the results with an outside antenna will be much better. In either case the antenna connects to an ordinary phone plug—soldered to the center terminal, which plugs into the phone jack on the set. Hook a ground, preferably a water pipe ground, to the ground terminal CL.

Turn on the set, and slowly advance the regeneration control on the end of the chassis. Suddenly, the hiss level will change tone and strength. This means the set has slipped into regeneration (oscillation). Rotate the main tuning capacitor. Chances are that you will pick up many "whistles" —some making a solid note, some keyed, because they are code stations. Experiment with the front panel regeneration control. You will note (assuming that it already was set at half-scale) that you can make the set slide in and out of regeneration using the front panel control—within the range of the band of frequencies covered by C-7.

Turn the capacitor C-6 all the way open, and adjust the regeneration controls until you can hear the set regenerating. Slowly turn the vernier dial on C-6 so the capacitor starts to close. About 10 degrees from the end you will probably hear some voice or music, with a whistle somewhat masking the signal. Slowly back off the regeneration control until the station becomes intelligible. Re-tune with the main tuning capacitor C-7. If all is well, you will be receiving your first short-wave broadcast station, very possibly foreign.

You will learn from working with the set that there are several bands of short wave broadcasting stations—with all kinds of things in between, including code stations, amateur SSB stations, etc. This set will tune the 25-meter, 31-meter, and 49-meter international broadcasting bands—and, depending on the exact dimensions of the coil, perhaps 19 meters as well.

You will find that the short-wave stations at the high end of the dial (capacitor C-6 almost open) come in best early in the evening, and that as darkness progresses, the stronger stations are at the lower frequencies.

Amateur Stations

There are two types of radio amateur stations: CW (continuous wave code) and SSB phone. The code stations are the easier to tune. In the amateur 40-meter band, which will come in at approximately "70" on the dial, you will hear these stations best with the regeneration control set so that the set is regenerating. Tune across the signal until the code is sharp and clean.

Commercial code stations are usually stronger—have a rough sound—and can be received with the regeneration control turned off. The code is also usually very fast, so fast that in many cases it can be received only by machine.

Practice with tuning short-wave broadcasting stations until you fully understand the inter-relation of the controls. You may find, for example, that as you cover the complete range of frequencies, some "dead spots" will occur at which the set will not regenerate. This can be overcome by opening up capacitor C-13. The objective of course, is to have a reasonable amount of capacity in use, but to reduce antenna coupling to the point where the set will break into regeneration at any setting of band-setting capacitor C-6. Also, you will learn that you want to advance the coarse regeneration control (RG-4, 5, 6) just enough to make the set regenerate, and then use the front panel control to drop in and out of regeneration as desired.

SSB Phone

Let's try our first amateur SSB station. Turn C-6 all of the way closed, which should result in your receiving the upper end of the 80-meter phone band at night. Advance the regeneration control until the set is barely oscillating in the regenerative condition. Tune with capacitor C-7. You will probably hear a number of stations which seem to be saying something, but which you cannot understand.

Pick one of moderate strength. Then, carefully, carefully, very carefully tune across the signal. At one extremely critical point—so critical that it is hard to believe—the gibberish will stop and you will be able to understand the station. Needless to say, some practice is necessary. If you tune in your first station within 20 minutes you will have accomplished something, indeed. However, once you get the idea, you will be able to pick up many stations quite easily. Two things will help—keep the antenna coupling as loose as possible (capacitor C-13 all the way open) and make minor adjustments of the "pitch" of the voice by making minor adjustments of the front panel regeneration control.

Learning to tune in SSB takes a bit of doing, but once you succeed you can listen in on amateur conversations by the hour, including foreign. You are more apt to find these, of course, in the higher-frequency 40-meter and 20-meter band—but 80 meters is the place to practice, since the tuning is much easier.

Refinements

You will probably find that both regeneration controls have to be all the way on to receive stations in the low end of the tuning range (down around 3.9 megacycles with C-6 almost all of the way closed) and that the controls are backed off considerably on the other end of the spectrum, with both tuning capacitors opened up. This is what should be—and if it is so, fine. However, you may find that you cannot get the set to oscillate (break into regeneration) at the low end, even with both controls advanced and with a minimum of antenna coupling. If this is the case, you need another turn or two on L-5, L-6. Try six turns first, and then seven, although the latter should seldom be necessary.

Conversely, you may discover that at the high end there appears to be too much regenerative feedback—the set breaks into regeneration with very little advancement of the controls—and if the controls are advanced very far, the set may go all the way into super-regeneration with miscellaneous squeals and howls and very broad tuning. If this can be kept in bounds by proper adjustment of the regeneration controls, don't worry—however, if it seems to be unmanageable, and there seems to be plenty of regeneration at the low end of the band, remove one turn from L-5 and L-6. The objective is to have the smallest number of turns on this coil which will allow regeneration with the tuning capacitors closed all of the way and the antenna tuning capacitor wide open.

Not as Tough as it Reads

Like so many things which require action, telling the "how" in words alone seems pretty difficult, for example, writing a manual on "how to ride a bicycle." But you can learn a lot in a hurry by actually doing the job—and tuning a shortwave receiver is no exception. You may brew up an amazing collection of whistles and howls at first—but before you know it you will be inviting some friend over to "hear South America direct"—and explaining that you do this all of the time!

CHAPTER 12

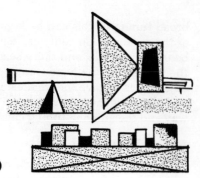

First Step to

Hi-Fi and Stereo

Seems like everybody wants hi-fi and stereo these days.

But what *is* hi-fi? Is that $24.95 two-speaker special sold by the local cut-rate drug store *actually* hi-fi? Or is it true—as some audiophiles will insist—that $500 will *barely* get you started?

Actually, it depends upon what you are talking about. Since hi-fi is by far the most controversial branch of electronics (with about as much witchcraft in it as science!), getting anybody to agree on a definition is almost impossible. The best thing to do is to define hi-fi, and let you take it from there.

Hi-Fi Is . . .

Hi-Fi is a method of reproducing records (or tape) so the reproduced sound sounds as much like the original as possible.

Notice that we didn't say "sounds *exactly* like." Even the most rabid hi-fi fan will admit—however reluctantly—that the best hi-fi setup ever built isn't as good as a seat in the front row of a symphony concert.

Although tape is sometimes used, records are still by far the more popular medium, particularly since the development of low-scratch, low-hiss vinyl records.

These records do a fair job of *recording* sound. *Reproducing* it is something else again. The first limitation is the cartridge. For the best possible quality, most dedicated hi-fi fans use special magnetic or moving-coil cartridges. These are quite expensive and have a very low output. However, even a high-output, low-cost crystal cartridge will reproduce a wide range of sounds— all the way from 30 cycles or so (a mighty low note indeed), to beyond 13,000 cycles (which a child can hear, but which is beyond the range of many adults).

The cartridge favored by audiophiles may reproduce from 10 to as much as 30,000 cycles—far above and below the normal hearing range. These do add some realism within the hearing range, so are worthwhile if nothing but the best will satisfy you. You'll pay dearly, of course. You won't have much change left from a $100 bill after you team the cartridge with a tone arm of the same quality.

The turntable is another vital link in the chain. It should be of very high quality, so that its speed will remain constant. Perfectionists generally shy away from changers, because even the best ones introduce some distortion. Nevertheless, some of the more expensive late-model changers do a pretty fair job. So the decision is really up to the individual.

Vocal Chords for Hi-Fi

The amplifier, which boosts the sound, comes in a wide variety of types, sizes, and costs. Ideally, the sound reproduced by a hi-fi amplifier will have a virtually flat response curve from below to above the audible range. Even so, an amplifier with less than perfect response still sounds good if everything else is working right.

What is left? Actually, only the speaker system. Note the word *system*. In hi-fi, it is common to go to considerable lengths in order to achieve an effective speaker arrangement—for example, using three types of speakers, all hooked to the same amplifier. These are a "tweeter," the tiny speaker which reproduces high notes especially well; a "midrange" speaker for the middle range of frequencies; and a "woofer," the large speaker that takes over when a bass viol or similar bass instrument generates the sound.

The speakers themselves are only part of the story. By enclosing the speaker or speakers in special cabinets, it is possible to enhance the reproduction.

That's what hi-fi is all about—simply a combination of highly-refined techniques which result in an almost lifelike reproduction of sound.

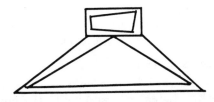

The best way to get started in hi-fi is to stick one toe in the water before plunging in. In other words, buy one piece of equipment at a time. Good hi-fi need not be expensive. Electronic gear can be rigged up quite economically, and the difference between it and an ordinary radio or small record player will be as noticeable as it is between an organ and a toy piano.

Perhaps this will be enough hi-fi to satisfy you. If not, you haven't wasted much money and have learned some practical pointers. Since a hi-fi system consists of a number of separate components hooked together, we can upgrade them one at a time. For example, we can replace an inexpensive changer with a hi-fi cartridge, tone arm, and turntable.

Back to our quick rundown of hi-fi techniques. Even a low-cost pickup and a record changer will reproduce sound better than most non-hi-fi owners ordinarily hear. It doesn't take much of an amplifier to do a fair job. But the place where a little extra effort and money make a tremendous difference is in the speaker system. So, for our first step to hi-fi, we'll devote our energies to the speaker hookup.

Fortunately, this isn't too difficult. Although the utimate is a whole string of speakers, extended-range speakers have been developed which do a good job by themselves. The smaller, eight-inch variety isn't too expensive. Likewise, we can build our own enclosure for the speaker.

Do-It-Yourself Enclosure

There are many types of enclosures, and as many opinions as to which is best. A speaker enclosure can be simple (a closed box with a vent) or complex (a bass reflex). A bass reflex enclosure certainly is good, but for maximum results the cabinet must be tuned to match the speaker resonant frequency—a somewhat tricky procedure, not recommended for your first venture into hi-fi.

The following cabinet is considerably larger than the base reflex for the same size of speaker, but although larger, is not critical of dimension and requires no tuning whatsoever. Such an enclosure is easy to build because it is simply a box, and you can do the job with only hand tools.

Furthermore, by making the box the same size as a bass reflex cabinet for a larger speaker, you can later cut larger holes in the cabinet and tune it, and be all set with a bass reflex enclosure. (This was done with the enclosure to be described.)

For 12-Inch Speakers, Too

This cabinet is designed for use with an extended-range, 16-ohm, 8-inch speaker. Later you can modify the enclosure easily and use it with a 12-inch extended-range unit, or perhaps a 12-inch woofer plus a midrange speaker and a tweeter.

The chief disadvantage of such an enclosure is its fairly large size. If you intend to use hi-fi in a small room, there is really only one practical way out—buy a ready-made compact enclosure, or build one from a kit. Such arrangements are elaborately "tuned" to simulate a larger cabinet. Whether they actually do is debatable, but certainly they sound better than no enclosure. In any event, choose a *16-ohm* extended-range speaker. *Do not* buy an 8-ohm speaker (more about this later).

We'll assume you are going to use your speaker in a basement family or rumpus room, in which case the enclosure will not be too large.

To build it, you'll have to obtain some ¾-inch plywood. The enclosure will take most of a 4- by 8-foot piece of plywood. You'll probably have to buy a full-size sheet, since most lumber yards usually take a dim view of chopping up large pieces and not charging for the scrap.

While at the lumber yard, you might as well have the panels cut to the dimensions in the drawings. The power saws available in a typical yard make the job easier, and insure square, clean cuts. If you must do the job yourself, use a sharp hand saw. Hook on a wooden guide strip with C clamps and saw alongside the strip, using it as a guide.

Since we want our box as solid and as airtight as possible, we will put it together by screwing and gluing the panels to 1-inch square wooden cleats.

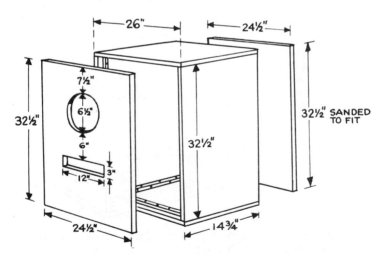

The drawings show the assembly, but a word or two will make the job easier.

☐ Cut eight 1-inch cleats to the following lengths: four, 13⅛", and four, 22½". The front and back panels will be mounted to the longer cleats; the side panels, to the shorter ones. Mount the two front and two side cleats ¾" from the edges of the top and bottom panels. Then mount the two back cleats 1" from the edges of the top and bottom panels. Glue the cleats to the panels, and reinforce every 6" with No. 7 flat-head (1¼") wood screws.

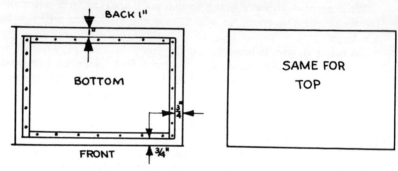

BACK 1"

BOTTOM

¾"

FRONT   ¾"

SAME FOR
TOP

☐ Next, screw the sides to the cleats. Make sure the frame is as square as possible. Remember to drill the screw holes in the cleats *before* you put the panels in place. Otherwise, you may have no room to work!

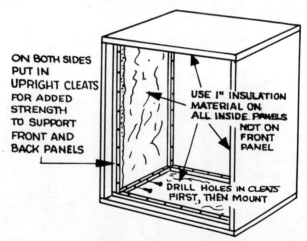

ON BOTH SIDES
PUT IN
UPRIGHT CLEATS
FOR ADDED
STRENGTH
TO SUPPORT
FRONT AND
BACK PANELS

USE 1" INSULATION
MATERIAL ON
ALL INSIDE PANELS
NOT ON
FRONT
PANEL

DRILL HOLES IN CLEATS
FIRST, THEN MOUNT

☐ Then slide the front panel in place. (This may require some sanding and fitting.)

☐ Now cut the back, making sure it can slide in and out. But don't fasten it down yet!

☐ Once the cabinet is done, you can cut the holes in the front, following the drawings. The easiest way is with a saber saw, if you are lucky enough to own such a saw (or can borrow one). Otherwise, drill a row of holes as a starter, and then finish the job with a keyhole saw. Fortunately, the holes will all be covered later, so they need not be flawless.

FRONT

GET BACK
PANEL ALIGNED—
SCREW THRU
PANEL INTO
CLEATS —
THEN REMOVE
FOR FURTHER
CONSTRUCTION

☐ Using the 16-ohm speaker as a guide (careful—a thumb through the cone will do it no good!), drill the holes for the speaker, and insert the bolts (No. 8-32 × 1¼″ ornamental head screws). Countersink the bolt heads flush with the panel surface.

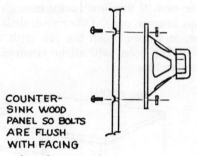

COUNTER-
SINK WOOD
PANEL SO BOLTS
ARE FLUSH
WITH FACING

☐ Make a frame of mahogany door casing for the front of the cabinet, as shown in the photograph and drawing. Apply clear varnish or lacquer, sanding between coats. Then give the frame a final sanding and waxing. Doing the finish job now will prevent your spilling varnish on the grille cloth later.

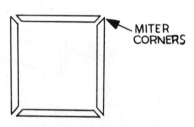

MITER
CORNERS

☐ Line the insides of the top, bottom, side, and back pieces with one-inch *Fiberglas* insulation. Use a staple gun (which you can borrow or rent from a lumber yard). The *Fiberglas* improves the over-all tonal quality.

☐ The cabinet finish will depend somewhat on your taste. Interior decorators recommend a color that matches the walls, or a contrasting color. Before painting, however, fill the cabinet and sand it thoroughly. A good filler is "joint" cement, used for joining panels in "dry wall" construction. Being sticky, it will stay put. Also, it sands to a smooth finish—so smooth it can hardly be told from wood.

☐ After the paint is dry, the next step is to install the grille cloth on the front. Attach the cloth along one edge of the panel by "tacking" it with a few dabs of all-purpose glue. Then mount one of the frame pieces, using small finishing nails. Stretch the cloth to eliminate any wrinkles, and attach it to the other three edges as before. Then nail on the remaining three frame pieces as before.

☐ Now mount the speaker, bolting it down tightly. Hook on the speaker lead (an ordinary light cord is fine), and run it through a hole in the back.

☐ Line the back cleats (onto which the back is attached) with a rubber gasket or weatherstripping. Screw on the back panel firmly against the stripping and the cleats. The idea is to have the box good and tight.

With our enclosure assembled, what else do we need?

Get Set for Stereo Later

First of all, we will need a record changer. Despite the unkind things the true hi-fi fan will say about an inexpensive changer, it is good enough for a starter. (It can be retired later for every-day use, or at parties when you want to protect a more valuable pickup from accidental damage!) Be sure it has a high-output crystal or ceramic cartridge, so you will not need a preamp to drive your amplifier. Or you can buy a stereo cartridge and continue using it when you change over to stereo later. The record changer for the system to be described has a 4-pole motor and a "compatible" crystal turnover cartridge (stereo, of course!).

When you buy the changer, also obtain a base for it if possible. If none is available, you can make one from a scrap of plywood and some wooden cleats. •

Now for connections to the changer. Underneath the changer you should find a terminal strip with four colored wires—red, black, blue, and yellow—running to it. (If not, see the instructions packed with your changer.)

The red and black pair is the right-hand stereo channel (R/H); the yellow and blue, the left-hand channel (L/H). For monaural hi-fi (our concern at this point), we'll *parallel* the two channels, as shown in the drawing. Red and yellow are "hot" leads carrying the signal. Follow the rest of the hookup. The other end of the shielded wire should terminate in a phono plug of the type used

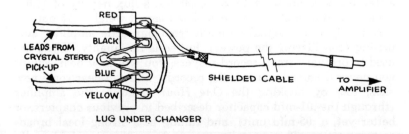

in other sets in this book—hot lead to center of plug, shield to rim. Incidentally, you can make your job much easier by buying a "harness" already wired up.

Fine! We now have a speaker and a record changer. But what about an amplifier?

Low-Power "Hi-Fi"

Believe it or not, you can use the utility amplifier you built earlier. This will astonish the "old hands," who will tell you the power output of an amplifier operated from a couple of flashlight batteries is too low to actuate a speaker.

However, the utility amplifier *will* work, and surprisingly well. Several points are in its favor. First of all, it is coupled directly to a speaker. There is no intervening transformer to waste power, so we can use it all. (Fortunately, the amplifier is capable of good-quality reproduction, even when run fairly wide open.) Also, by using an extended-range speaker, we waste no power on crossover networks or tone controls. So we treat our one-third watt or so very kindly.

But can you hear anything?

With the volume all the way up, the sound from many records will be uncomfortably loud at the far end of a 12- by 40-foot room . . . so loud, in fact, that you may get a firm request from upstairs to "turn that thing down!" Skeptical? You will be, until you've tried it.

Eventually, of course, you will want to build a far more powerful amplifier from one of the many kits on the market. But at the start, the utility amplifier will give you a lot of pleasure at a low cost. Later, you can retire it to one of its other purposes—for example, as a signal tracer or in a call system.

Two items are important in using the utility amplifier as the final link in our hi-fi system: (1) the phono cartridge must be a crystal or other high-output type, and (2) the speaker must be a 16-ohm extended-range unit, with a husky magnet and good sensitivity (these are the marks of a good speaker, the only kind you should buy). The speaker chosen for the original model had a frequency response of 40 to 18,000 cps, a flux density of 13,000 gausses, and a 16-ohm voice coil. The magnet weighed 15 ounces.

Not only is the signal strength from our little amplifier surprising (considering the power), but so is the quality. If you are used to ordinary small record players, you will now hear sounds you never dreamed were on the records. You can hear some new ones, too, by hooking the *One Hour* radio to the amplifier (through the .01-mfd capacitor described in previous chapters, or better yet, a .05-mfd unit), and tuning in a strong local broadcasting station. The crystal set reproduces the signal virtually as it is broadcast. Hence, the set is a kind of hi-fi tuner. When it is played through a good amplifier and speaker, its tonal quality can only be described as astounding, compared with that of an ordinary table-model radio.

Several pointers may help you get the most from the small amplifier. First of all, you can hike the battery voltage to 4.5 volts by adding another cell (but at a severe sacrifice of battery life).

Because 390K resistor R (in series with the incoming signal) has a pronounced effect on the tonal quality, its value must match that of the changer pickup. If there are too many "highs," raise the value of this resistor. (Try 0.5-, 1-, 2-, and 5-meg units.) If the changer sounds all right as is, try *lower* values (250K, 100K, 50K). The idea is to use the lowest value that does not upset the quality, because the resistor tends to cut down on the incoming signal.

You may like the little amplifier so much that you want to make it into a semi-permanent hookup. If so, it would be convenient to eliminate the batteries, which you can do by building a power supply. Notice that the power transformer reduces the voltage to 6.3 volts. This voltage is rectified by a silicon rectifier and then filtered. After further filtering by a transistor, virtually pure DC is delivered—exactly the substitute we need for the batteries. Of course, the batteries are removed when the power supply is hooked to the set. Be careful to also observe the polarity of the supply. Incidentally, this power-supply circuit was first publicized by I. Queen, who deserves the full credit for the circuit.

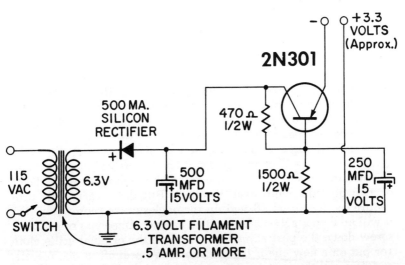

Eventually you will probably tire of your flea-powered hi-fi and decide to build an amplifier (preferably stereo) from a kit. If so, you'll want to use the speaker enclosure for a larger speaker. Here is a brief rundown on how to tune the bass reflex cabinet to match a 12-inch extended-range or similar speaker.

First, remove the framing and grille cloth from the front, and cut the front panel to new dimensions shown in the drawing. Fit the bottom vent with a sliding cover, as illustrated. This device makes it possible to tune the enclosure to match the speaker.

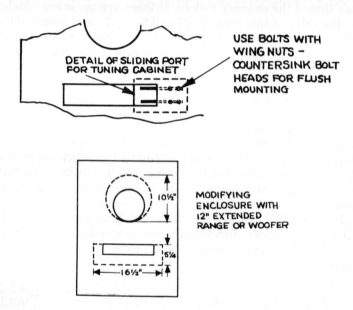

DETAIL OF SLIDING PORT
FOR TUNING CABINET

USE BOLTS WITH
WING NUTS –
COUNTERSINK BOLT
HEADS FOR FLUSH
MOUNTING

MODIFYING
ENCLOSURE WITH
12" EXTENDED
RANGE OR WOOFER

Mount the 12-inch speaker, and hook up your changer and amplifier. Put on a test record (the kind giving a slow sweep of frequencies from about 20 to 200 cycles or so). Replace the back.

Leave the vent (also called a *port*) wide open, and listen carefully. As the record plays through the frequency range, the signal will seem to "peak up" at one (maybe two) points, and the speaker will have a booming sound. Keep making the vent smaller, until the "boomy" peaks are as low as you can get them.

You can "touch up" the adjustment by adding an extra layer or two of grille cloth over the port. But don't carry this procedure too far, or you'll seal up the enclosure so thoroughly that it will no longer act as a bass reflex cabinet. Once you're satisfied, screw down the port adjustment, replace the original grille cloth (or put on a new one if the old one didn't peel off in one piece!), and reinstall the frame.

Stereo—For People With Two Ears

From the sample hi-fi just described, you can decide whether you want to go on. If you do, good luck! Make each new move cautiously, reading up on the subject *before* you sink too much money into it. Read at least *two* books because, as we have said, hi-fi is laced with opinions.

True hi-fi enthusiasts are never satisfied with a simple record player-amplifier-speaker hookup because it is *monaural*—a high-toned way of saying *single-sound*. In nature, few sounds *are* single-sound. Moreover, most of us hear all sound with *two* ears.

For these two reasons, scientists toyed with the idea of recording two sound tracks on one record. The first effort was to combine the old "hill-and-dale" (in which the needle moves up and down) with the newer "lateral" method (in which the needle moves back and forth). There were a lot of technical problems, however, although the British were able to whip most of them.

Not too long ago, the Westrex Company came up with the real answer—a **V**-shaped record groove. Both *sides* of the **V** are used—the right one for the right channel; the left one for the left

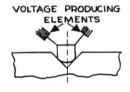

VOLTAGE PRODUCING ELEMENTS

UNMODULATED GROOVE, NO OUTPUT GENERATED

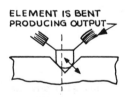

ELEMENT IS BENT PRODUCING OUTPUT

RIGHT SIDE MODULATED, OUTPUT FROM RIGHT ELEMENT ONLY

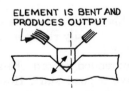

ELEMENT IS BENT AND PRODUCES OUTPUT

LEFT SIDE MODULATED, OUTPUT FROM LEFT ELEMENT ONLY

channel. The diagram shows how this works. *Two* sources can thus be recorded at the same time. In like fashion, two amplifiers and speakers can be played at the same time. Hence, we have two sound sources.

You Are There . . .

The net result is that the two amplifier systems play different portions of the original sound source. The sound seems to "surround" you, giving the illusion of an orchestra in the same room with you. The reason, of course, is that you hear an orchestra from a broad source, not from one point.

Although you can get by with *one* pickup and tone arm in stereo, from there on you have to duplicate everything else—two preamplifiers (if your hookup includes one, two amplifiers, and two speaker systems).

One of the peculiarities of stereo is that it is mighty hard to tell *where* low-frequency sounds are coming from. (This is one reason we whistle to call a dog; it can follow a whistle better than it can a shout.) This means we don't need high quality to get stereo. Not that good equipment isn't desirable, however—it is. But it isn't necessary.

One approach is to place one large speaker in the center, and feed *both* stereo channels into it. Then the big speaker is flanked right and left with small speakers capable of reproducing those frequencies which give the stereo effect. The smaller speakers, driven by the right and left channels from the pickup, save the expense of having two large ones. They also put plenty of horsepower into the big speaker, where it is useful for those room-rattling bass notes.

It is not within the scope of this book to detail a complicated hi-fi stereo system. However, you can easily rig up a simple stereo layout which will amaze your friends!

Assuming we have the recommended record changer with a stereo cartridge, we already have a good start. However, we'll have to "break" the lead connecting the two sides of the stereo cartridge in parallel, and also provide a volume control and a series resistor for the new "hot" lead. We'll need all these for a more elaborate arrangement later, so we might as well get them now.

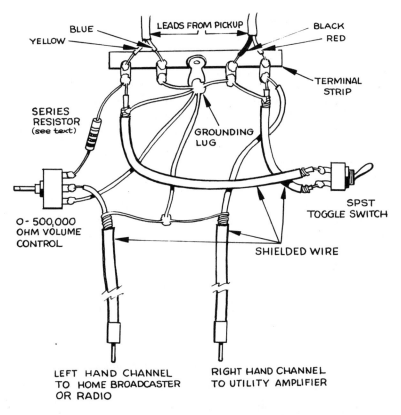

LEADS FROM PICKUP

BLUE
YELLOW
BLACK
RED

TERMINAL STRIP

SERIES RESISTOR
(see text)

GROUNDING LUG

SPST TOGGLE SWITCH

0 - 500,000 OHM VOLUME CONTROL

SHIELDED WIRE

LEFT HAND CHANNEL TO HOME BROADCASTER OR RADIO

RIGHT HAND CHANNEL TO UTILITY AMPLIFIER

MODIFYING CHANGER TO USE ON STEREO

The drawing shows the new terminal-strip hookup. Notice that we separate the red and yellow leads, giving us two outputs—the R/H and the L/H channel. We put in a switch so we can revert to regular monaural audio at any time.

Both the volume control and the monaural-stereo switch can be mounted on the base of the record player. As you will see, the hookup also includes a resistor in series with the L/H channel. This resistor should be the right value for our particular crystal pickup, as determined by experiment earlier in the chapter.

Quick 'N Easy Stereo

We've wound up with two 2-wire leads from the changer. One, of course, goes to the utility amplifier and its speaker. Fit the other lead (L/H channel) with a suitable plug, and connect in place of the microphone on our home broadcaster. We use the home broadcaster to put a signal into a table-model radio (which should be 10 feet or so to the *left* of our speaker system). Now, fire up the home broadcaster, the radio, and the changer; and tune in the signal.

Adjust the volume controls on the radio and record changer for the most satisfactory volume and quality. Then adjust the amplifier volume control until the volume from the two units is roughly the same. At this point (assuming the record has a pronounced stereo effect), you should hear the sound alternately from one side and the other.

If you *really* want to hear realism, you can buy recordings of a bowling ball thundering down an alley, a train roaring by, the screeching of brakes—ideal for showing off your stereo outfit.

Of course, the quality of our temporary setup is pretty poor, because we're losing all along the line—the home broadcaster is not quite a broadcasting station, its transformers are far from high fidelity, etc. So, for anything except an experiment, we should at least go one more step and feed our signal directly inside our radio. In this way, we can at least get as much out of the radio as it is capable of reproducing.

Tapping Into a Radio

The typical AC-DC radio has enough gain to reproduce the output from a crystal cartridge. For this reason, we can use it as a simple amplifier for our left channel.

Before tackling this job, though, some words of caution. One of the reasons for using transistor equipment up to now is that it is safe. Now, for the first time, we'll be delving into something potentially lethal. *There is the possibility of your being electrocuted if you don't watch your step.* Conversely, if you are careful, there is no danger whatsoever.

The risk stems from the fact that many parts—and sometimes even the chassis—of an AC-DC radio are connected to a 110-volt power line. Touching a "hot" part while the set is on and your body is contacting a ground (such as the basement floor) will put the full power-line voltage through your body. This voltage could kill you.

So, start out with this danger always in mind. *Before* you do anything, *pull the plug—don't* just turn off the switch.

Next, take the set apart, so you can get at the underside of the chassis. Usually this involves pulling off the knobs and removing the screws or bolts securing the chassis to the cabinet. Be careful not to break off any speaker (or other) leads as you slide the set from its cabinet.

The "Why" Plus the "How"

Before we dive into the chassis, let's be certain we've decided exactly what we are going to do.

Just like a transistor radio, a table-model radio has a driver (or first audio amplifier) and a power-amplifier stage. Ninety-nine times out of one hundred, the drive stage is fed from the movable arm of the volume control. The signal is amplified by the driver stage, and this amplified signal is again boosted in the power-output stage.

Ordinarily, our signal would be coming from the detector in the radio. In order to use the amplifier portion as a phono amplifier, however, we must cut the detector loose from the amplifier portion. Otherwise, we'll get two signals at once (quite a mess!). Besides, the diode detector contributes a clipping action which does our quality no good at all.

So, we disconnect the regular lead going from the volume control to the grid of the driver tube. This lead is connected by either a fixed capacitor or one section of a couplet. (A couplet is a ceramic capacitor or two with molded-in resistor elements and a number of leads.)

Next, run the volume-control lead to one side of a SPDT switch. The other side of the switch goes to a phono pickup jack, so we can feed the amplifier in the *set* from its own detector, or else from the left channel of our record-changer cartridge. The *center* of our three-terminal switch goes to the couplet, which in turn goes to the grid of the audio stage.

Watch This One

One more point—and it is extremely important.

We need to complete the circuit (as well as shield the various leads from stray AC pickup, which can cause hum) by grounding the shielded wire used for the various connections. As mentioned,

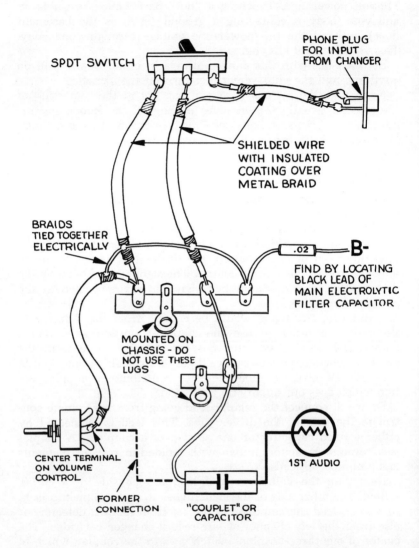

SPDT SWITCH

PHONE PLUG
FOR INPUT
FROM CHANGER

SHIELDED WIRE
WITH INSULATED
COATING OVER
METAL BRAID

BRAIDS
TIED TOGETHER
ELECTRICALLY

.02   **B-**

FIND BY LOCATING
BLACK LEAD OF
MAIN ELECTROLYTIC
FILTER CAPACITOR

MOUNTED ON
CHASSIS - DO
NOT USE THESE
LUGS

1ST AUDIO

CENTER TERMINAL
ON VOLUME
CONTROL

FORMER
CONNECTION

"COUPLET" OR
CAPACITOR

HOOK UP FOR ADDING PHONO
JACK TO AC-DC RADIO —

however, the ground in an AC-DC radio can be lethal, since it is one side of the 110-volt line.

We can get around this hazard by grounding through a fixed capacitor *only*, as shown in the drawing. The "shields" on the shielded wire, which are all connected together, are grounded through a .02-mfd fixed capacitor .

Mount both the switch and the jack on the cardboard back of the set, or on the plastic case or other well-insulated spot. The drawing shows the wiring hookup.

Be careful when using the shielded wire. First of all, it should have an insulating cover *over* the braided shield. Otherwise, there is a danger of accidentally shorting to some "hot" lead, or some similar mishap.

Too, the plastic insulation inside is usually pretty soft. Unless you are careful in soldering, it may melt and short the center wire to the shield. This, of course, will kill the signal.

The Life You Save Could Be Your Own!

After completing the hookup as shown, reassemble the set. Now, we'll test to see if the phono jack is safe.

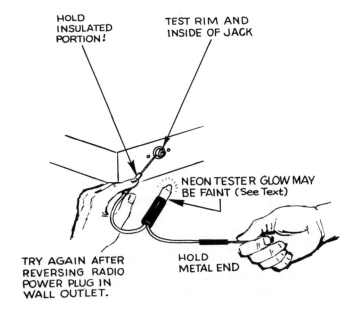

An easy way to do this is to use a neon bulb tester. Grasp one bare test lead in one hand. Gripping the other end *by the insulated portion,* touch first the "rim" of the plug and then the center of the phono jack. Reverse the plug of the radio in the wall, and repeat the procedure. If the bulb does not glow, there is no voltage on the jack—exactly what we want.

If the plug checks out all right, the next step is to see if we can run the radio with the changer. Plug the L/H lead into the phono plug jack on the back of our modified AC-DC radio. First, tune in a station, just to make certain the radio is working properly. Then tune *off* the station, to a quiet spot on the dial, and throw the switch on the back of the set. This hooks the set to the record changer.

With the changer playing, you should now hear the record on the radio. The loudness is controlled by the volume control we added to the changer.

Setting Up For Stereo

If everything is working properly, we now have a left channel. The next step is to arrange our speakers about ten feet apart and facing us. We'll drive the right speaker with the utility amplifier, as before.

Play a stereo record, and adjust the volume on both units until it is about equal. The stereo effect should be apparent, especially on a stereo demonstration record.

There is just one more adjustment. Reverse the leads going from the speaker system to the utility amplifier. One connection may give better quality than the other.

"Wind-up"

These setups are about the minimum which will give a stereo effect. If you are seriously interested, you will most certainly want to build a stereo amplifier from a kit.

There is at least one kit available (and reasonably priced) which operates from a crystal or ceramic pickup and delivers 3 watts on both channels. Although not a whopping amount of audio, it is a lot more than our utility amplifier provides, and will do nicely for your first stereo setup. The 8-inch speaker system already described is adequate for a simple layout. To handle the other channel, simply duplicate it.

A $24.95 drugstore "hi-fi" was mentioned at the beginning of the chapter. We'll agree now that such a rig isn't hi-fi. A speaker and a homemade enclosure alone will cost more than this. But the $500 figure isn't right, either. If you will settle for something less than perfection, you can do the job for a fraction of that amount. Happy listening!

CHAPTER 13

Stereo Amplifier

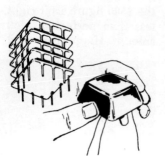

Uses Modules

As mentioned in the previous chapter, what we need for stereo is two of everything: a stereo pick-up that will provide both channels, a pair of amplifiers, and a pair of speakers.

Of course, one way to do this is to use two of the utility amplifiers, plus two of the speakers with enclosures like those described in the previous chapter. However, if you are serious about stereo, a better approach is to build an honest-to-goodness stereo amplifier. Actually "amplifier" is not quite the right word because for stereo purposes we use two identical amplifiers, one for each channel.

These may be highly sophisticated and expensive units, a bit beyond the building skill of the beginner in electronics. But thanks to the development of modules, building a stereo system that will yield pleasant listening at satisfactory volume for the average room is surprisingly easy. The twin amplifier stereo unit to be described in this chapter has only a few more parts than the single channel utility amplifier described earlier.

A Word About Modules

More and more the word "module" is mentioned in electronic literature, and with good reason, because modules offer many advantages. Actually, the term is rather broad in meaning—it usually refers to a unit that is a complete electronic circuit, and which in most cases requires some kind of input signal, some kind of output device such as a loudspeaker, and some kind of a power supply.

Modules save wiring time for the builder, and usually cost no more than the same number of parts purchased separately. In complex manufactured devices—for example, color television sets —the module frequently provides for quicker servicing. By isolating the trouble to the portion of the set served by one module,

the service man can make the repair by replacing the module. This frequently takes far less time than isolating the individual part causing the trouble.

The photo shows one kind of module that contains all of the parts needed for an audio amplifier. The complete amplifier is encased in epoxy, and is almost the size of a golf ball. Actually, the module is designed as a phono amplifier, and if it is fed with a high output monaural crystal pick-up it will, by itself, step up the signal to the point of comfortable room listening. For use with a

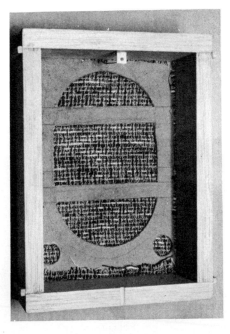

crystal or ceramic stereo pick-up, which usually has less output than a monaural cartridge, we need a bit more drive. In the unit

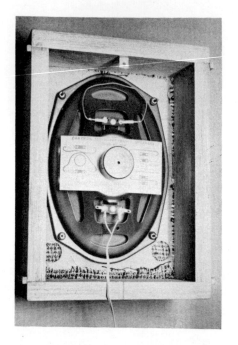

to be discussed, this is provided by a one-stage transistor amplifier that serves as a driver stage.

Power for the stereo system comes from two batteries, one for each of the amplifiers. The use of batteries eliminates the need for building a power supply, and simplifies the overall project considerably. Battery life is kept within reason by utilizing 40-ohm oval speakers of the type frequently used as "rear seat" speakers in car radios. The speakers are mounted in very simple wooden enclosures approximately 3 inches thick and generally hung on the wall like a picture. The signal quality, of course, does not compare with that of the speaker and enclosure described earlier—however, it compares favorably with many of the "under $75.00" commercial portable stereo outfits. The speaker enclosure is easy and practical to build with the simplest of tools. The speakers can, of course, be place on a table or shelf rather than hung on a wall like a picture.

The use of batteries does make the stereo system completely portable, and by mounting the amplifier with its batteries in a small case, the outfit would be ideal for picnics or beach parties if used with a battery-operated record player.

Shopping List

Here is the list of the parts you will need to build the easy stereo amplifier:

Quantity	Description	In Drawing Part Labeled:
1	7"x7" aluminum chassis, 2" deep	
2	RCA type 2-conductor audio jack	Ph
2	1/2-watt 270,000 (270K)-ohm 1/2-watt resistor (see text)	A
2	2-mfd 25-volt electrolytic capacitor	B
2	Terminal strip with 3 insulated lugs	C
2	120,000 (120 K)-ohm 1/2-watt resistor	D
2	10,000 (10 K)-ohm 1/2-watt resistor	E
2	100-mfd 25-volt electrolytic capacitor	F

Quantity	Description	In Drawing Part Labeled:
2	2200 (2.2 K)-ohm 1/2 watt resistor	G
2	Terminal strips with one grounded and two insulated lugs	H
2	5-mfd 25-volt electrolytic capacitor	I
2	10,000 (10 K)-ohm 1/2-watt resistors	J
2	50,000-ohm volume control with spst switch	K
2	Terimnal strip with one or more grounded and two insulated terminals	L
2	PH-7 Module (Mfg. by Carl Cordover & Co., Mineola, New York)	Mod
2	PNP audio transistor (2N107) or for more gain: (SK3004)	TRN
4	2-terminal screw-type terminal strip	T
2	Knobs for volume control	
4	Rubber grommets for 1/4" hole	
Misc.	Nuts and bolts	
Misc.	Hook-up wire and 2-wire speaker cable	
2	6-volt lantern battery	
2	10/20/40-ohm 6" x 9" oval speaker, preferably extended range type	

One Stage at a Time

The module stereo amplifier is an ideal project for the beginner because it can be broken down into building units so small that there should be little chance for making a wiring mistake. Although the amplifier is actually two amplifiers, each can be built (and tested) separately. We can build the driver stage of one am-

plifier, and test it to see if it is functioning satisfactorily before adding the module output portion.

Building . . .

The first step, of course, is to mount the various parts. The sketches and photos show where the parts go. There will be less chance of damage to parts if all holes for the larger parts are made before the parts are mounted.

Drill the 3/8" holes for the volume controls that go along the front of the chassis. If you have only a hand drill, which will handle bits only up to 1/4", the hole can be enlarged with a small file, or with a reamer like that illustrated.

Next, drill the holes for phono jack connectors. The easiest way to do this is to drill the large hole first, and then, with the jack in the hole, use the jack itself as a template to locate the centers of the smaller holes needed for nuts and bolts that secure the jack to the chassis. Use an ice pick or other sharp tool to punch the aluminum lightly, both to mark the holes and to provide a pilot hole for drilling.

Finally, cut the holes for the 2-terminal screw-type terminal strips. Again, the strip itself can be used to locate the holes needed for mounting bolts. However, in addition, it is necessary to provide a rectangular opening to keep the terminal lugs from shorting to the chassis. This is done by drilling a couple of 1/4" holes, and then, with a round file and finally a flat file, cutting out the opening. Be certain that the terminals do not touch the chassis—modules can be ruined if this happens and voltage is applied.

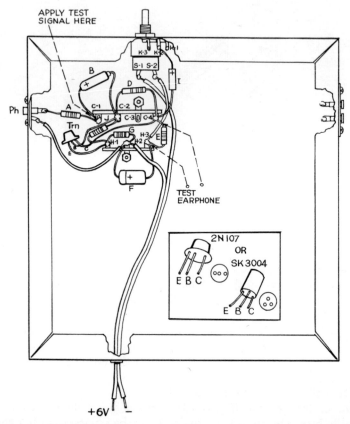

The holes for the grommets are easy to install—simply drill 1/4″ holes at the proper point. Push the grommets into the holes with a screwdriver. The terminal strips such as "C" require only 5/32″ holes to handle machine screws and nuts.

Parts Layout

- [ ] Mount the two volume controls on the front of the chassis, utilizing the nuts that come with them.
- [ ] Mount the screw-type terminal strips on one side of the chassis. Again be certain that the terminal parts do not touch the chassis.
- [ ] Using 6-32 nuts and bolts, mount the audio jacks.
- [ ] Again, using nuts and bolts, mount the terminal strips.

Wiring

Before starting, check the parts. Be certain that the color codes indicate the proper sizes of resistors.

- [ ] Connect one end of resistor A (270K) to center terminal phone jack Ph (S).
- [ ] Connect other end of resistor A to lug C-1 (DS).
- [ ] Connect "plus" end of capacitor B (2mfd) to lug C-1 (S).
- [ ] The opposite end of capacitor B goes to lug C-2 (DS).
- [ ] Secure one end of resistor D (120K) to lug C-2 (DS).
- [ ] With pliers, connect opposite end of D to lug C-4 (DS).
- [ ] Run one end of resistor E (10K) from lug C-4 (DS) to lug H-3 (DS).
- [ ] From H-3 (DS) run a lead to switch S-2 on volume control K (S).
- [ ] Connect "minus" end of capacitor "F" (100 mfd) to lug H-3 (S).
- [ ] Connect "plus" end of capacitor "F" to lug H-2 (DS).
- [ ] From lug H-2, run resistor G (2.2K) (DS) to lug H-1 (DS).
- [ ] Hook resistor J (10K) to lug H-1 (DS).
- [ ] Run opposite end of J to lug C-2 (DS).
- [ ] Connect a lead from H-2 (DS) to the off-center "ground" lug on jack Ph (S).

Adding the Transistor

Soldering a transistor into a circuit is always a critical point because of the possible danger to the transistor from the heat of the soldering iron. As illustrated earlier in the book, one way to do the job is to protect the transistor by gripping the lead with pliers between the soldering iron and the body of the transistor.

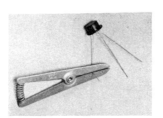

The difficulty of this approach is that you really need three hands—one for solder, one for the soldering iron, and one for the pliers. This problem has been solved though, with the use of a "heat sink" tool that clamps on the transistor and absorbs the heat. The tool shown is only one of several types—they all have some spring-tension device for gripping a transistor lead, thus freeing one hand for other things.

Identify the "emitter" lead of the transistor. The drawing shows how the leads are arranged on the 2N107—other transistors have different arrangements and some details on them are given in the final section of the book.

- ☐ Hook "emitter" lead to lug H-1. Apply heat sink tool to transistor lead between body of transistor and the point being soldered. Solder the lead to lug H-1. Allow it to cool before removing tool.
- ☐ Hook "base" lead to C-2. Again, using the heat sink tool for protection, solder.
- ☐ In the same manner, hook the "collector" to lug C-4 (DS).
- ☐ Connect minus end of capacitor I (5 mfd) to lug C-4. With the heat sink on transistor lead, solder.
- ☐ Solder "plus" end of condenser I to lug K-2 on the 50K volume control.

Adding the Power Leads

This is another ticklish point in our wiring, because there must be no error in hooking up the battery. Reversing polarity to a transistor may ruin it. For our power "cable" we will use a short length of flexible 2-wire (lamp cord) speaker extension wire. This wire is flat and flexible, and has an added advantage in that one of the wires is identified in some manner. This means that we can keep track of the leads which must be labeled plus and minus.

- ☐ Run a length of the wire through the grommet provided, long enough so that you have plenty of wire with which to work. Tie a knot in the wire inside the chassic so that if pull is placed on the power lead it puts force on the grommet and not on the wiring inside.
- ☐ Solder the plus lead to the lug H-2 which grounds to the chassis.
- ☐ Solder the minus lead to S-1 switch terminal on volume control.

This completes the wiring of the power leads of the amplifier. Check and re-check the wiring for errors. Look for poorly-soldered joints, particularly where several leads go to one lug, for example, on H-3, H-2, C-2, or C-4. It is very easy to have one wire fail to solder properly, and usually this can be found only by careful examination and by pulling and tugging on the lead. If you have any doubt—re-solder.

TESTING FIRST TRANSISTOR STAGE

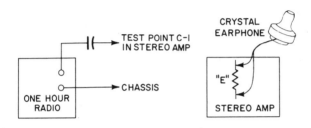

Signal Insertion for Testing

To test the transistor stage, we need to connect the lantern battery with the switch in the *off* position. Remember that one side of

BLOCK DIAGRAM-STEREO HOOK-UP

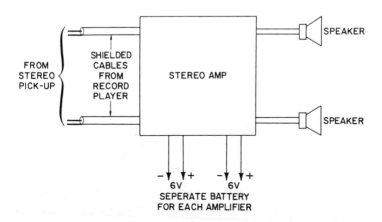

the flat flexible wire is connected to the "plus 6 volts" and the other lead to the minus.

We need to hook a high impedance *crystal* earphone across resistor "E," using clips and leads, as indicated in Chapter 10. Now, we need a signal source, and for this purpose our One Hour Radio is ideal, and can be used as was described in Chapter 10. Apply a clip lead from the output side of the .01 capacitor to the test signal point indicated in the drawing. Another clip lead is run from the "ground" side of the One Hour Radio to the chassis of the stereo amplifier.

The block diagram shows the overall hookup for testing the transistor amplifier stage. Of course, the One Hour Radio is only one possible signal source—any type of small signal generator can be used instead. Transistorized signal injectors are ideal. Chapter 14 covers this in more detail.

Turn the switch on. If everything is working properly, you will hear the signal from the One Hour Radio, considerably amplified. To see if the transistor stage is adding gain, apply the test signal to C-4. The signal should be considerably weaker, since at this point the transistor is contributing no amplification.

If the transistor stage is amplifying, you are ready to wire the next stage. If not, apply service techniques as described in Chapter 14 to locate the trouble.

Wiring the Module Stage

Look at the module from the bottom. This shows the layout of the leads.

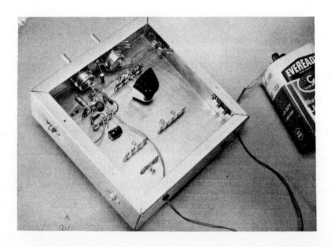

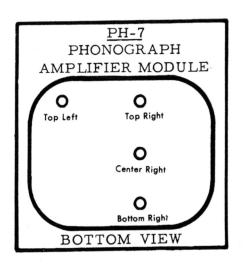

PH-7
PHONOGRAPH
AMPLIFIER MODULE

Top Left   Top Right

Center Right

Bottom Right

BOTTOM VIEW

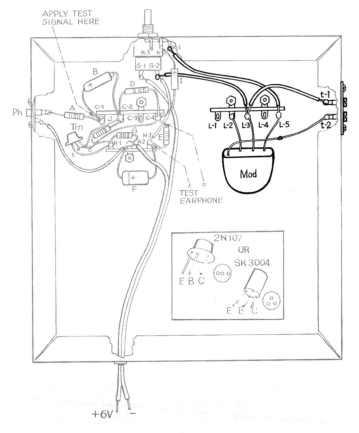

- [ ] Protecting the module with a heat sink, solder the *top right* lead to lug L-2. This is the lug grounded to the chassis.
- [ ] Connect a short lead to t-2, the screw terminal strip (S).
- [ ] Run the other end of the wire to the *top left* lead. Use a heat sink and solder.
- [ ] Solder one end of a lead to S-2, being careful not to destroy the connections made previously.
- [ ] Run the other end of the lead to lug L-3 (DS).
- [ ] With heat sink in place, hook module lead *center right* to terminal L-3 (DS).
- [ ] From L-3 (S) run a lead to t-1 (S).
- [ ] Connect *bottom right* to L-5 (DS).
- [ ] Connect lead from K-1 (S) and other end to L-5 (S).

STEREO AMPLIFIER (one channel)

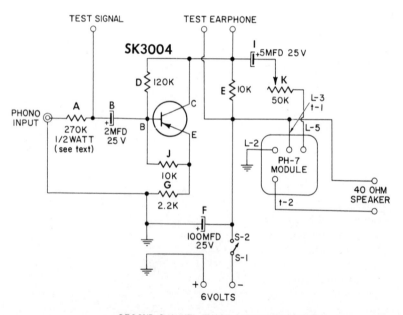

SECOND CHANNEL EXACT DUPLICATE OF FIRST

This completes the wiring—we are now ready to hook the amplifier to a speaker.

As mentioned previously, the speaker chosen for the unit is a 6x9 oval unit—the type used for rear seat extensions for car radio. These speakers are so arranged that their impedances can be adjusted—usually 10/20/40 ohms. We want to use the 40-ohm adjustment, in order to give the maximum resistance available. This

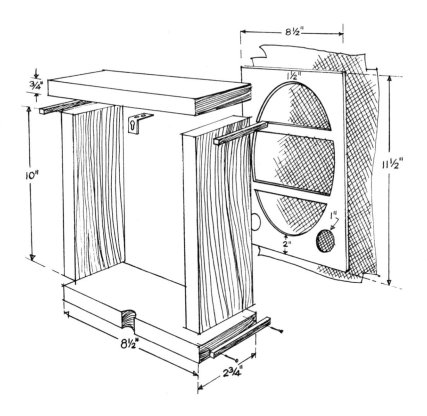

ensures longer battery life, and also reduces chances of the module overheating. Ordinarily, there is a chart packed with the speaker which gives the hook-up for the desired impedance.

To mount our speakers, we need some type of enclosure. The one shown will win no awards for fine furniture—but is so simple to build that virtually anyone can do it.

As shown in the drawing, the enclosure consists of a wooden frame, with a tempered *Masonite* front panel. The frame is made of standard "one-inch" Philippine mahogany, which actually measures approximately 3/4″ thick. If you do not have a power saw, you can do as the writer did, and have the boards cut at a lumber yard. By getting good, squared cuts, assembly of the frame is much easier.

Put the frame together with finishing nails and white glue. The nail holes can be filled with a mahogany-colored plastic wood. Note that small "style strips" are added. These serve to cover the joint and act as "feet" if the enclosure is placed on a shelf.

The *Masonite* front panel is cut out to allow for sound passage. The exact size and shape of the cut-outs is unimportant, simply follow the photograph. After this is done, the panel is covered with a piece of grill cloth. Actually, any loosely woven cloth could be used. As shown, the cloth is wrapped around the edge of the board and glued to the panel.

The mahogany frame should be finished before the panel is affixed to it. This is accomplished with glue and very small finishing nails. If you use small nails, they will tend to bury themselves in the grill cloth, and not be visible from the front. If desired, the enclosure can be given a more finished look by framing the front panel as was done with the enclosure described in Chapter 12.

A small metal angle strip is mounted on one end of the enclosure so that it can be hung up on the wall on a small nail or picture hook. Note that there is a half-round slot on the frame (put there with a rattail file) so that the speaker extension wire can be run down the wall without pushing the speaker away from the wall. The speaker itself is mounted to the front panel of the enclosure by means of 6/32 ornamental machine screws and nuts. Use washers or grommets under the nuts, since most speakers have fairly large mounting holes. You can use the speaker itself as a template for determining where the holes should be—however, be careful not to accidentally punch a hole through the cone. Follow the diagram that comes with the speaker to make whatever connections are necessary to provide an impedance of 40 ohms.

Testing the System

If the transistor driver stage tested out satisfactorily, chances are good that you are in business. The module stage is so simple that there should be little chance for a wiring error. However, before hooking up the battery, take a good look, and be certain that the unit has been wired exactly as shown.

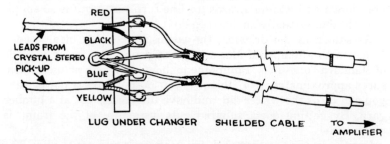

LUG UNDER CHANGER   SHIELDED CABLE   TO → AMPLIFIER

Plug in the shielded cable lead from the record player. Assuming it is a stereo unit, there will be two leads—either will do for the initial test. If you are using a record player modified as described in Chapter 12 for use with the home broadcaster in a stereo hook-up, you will need to re-wire the player as shown in the diagram.

Hook the speaker to output terminals t-1 and t-2. Start the record player. Turn on the volume control switch on the amplifier and turn up the volume. You should hear the record player instantly—transistors require no warm-up time. If you hear nothing, shut the unit off quickly, and start trouble-shooting.

First, be certain that the record player is "putting out." This is easily determined by connecting a crystal earphone to the output plug from the player. One earphone lead should be connected (with the ever-useful clip leads) to the center terminal of the phono plug, and the other to the outside of the plug which is wired to the braid of the shielded lead.

Assuming that you do have a signal from the record player, isolating the trouble should not be difficult since the module is about the simplest electronic device possible. Follow test procedures as outlined in Chapter 14.

Now—Do It All Again

Once you have one amplifier working, all you have to do to complete your stereo amplifier is duplicate the original. You can follow the same step-by-step wiring instructions right down to the point of adding capacitor "F." Actually, the wiring is electrically the same from there on, as well. However, for convenience in mounting parts, there is a minor change in layout.

☐ As before, connect the minus end of capacitor "I" (5 mfd) to lug H-3. With a heat sink on transistor lead, solder.

- [ ] Run "plus" end of capacitor "I" to lug L-1 (DS).
- [ ] From L-1, run a wire (S) to lug K-1 (S).

The power lead is connected exactly as for the first unit. Over-all check-out procedures are also the same.

For Listening

As with any stereo hook-up, this one will work best if the speakers are separated a reasonable distance, say 10 feet, although the stereo effect will be noticeable with shorter spacing. Adjust the volume controls so that the sound output appears to be about the same from either speaker. If you are not certain which of the leads from the phono pick-up is the right or left channel, try reversing them as plugged into the amplifier to see which way gives the more pleasing sound.

The input resistor A is used to reduce the "highs"—and the value required will depend upon the phono pick-up in use. The ideal is to use the lowest value that results in satisfactory tone quality, since the resistor drops volume considerably. Experiment with 100K, 200K, and 470K. The last-named value, of course, will reduce volume below the level of that with the resistor recommended in the parts list, but might be required with some pick-ups.

If you do need the high value, it will be best to use the SK3004 transistor for the driver stage, instead of the 2N107. The former has somewhat more gain.

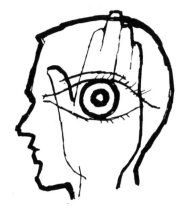

CHAPTER 14

Playing Detective in Electronic Circuits

Troubleshooting a piece of electronic gear requires (1) knowledge of electronics and (2) an orderly *method*.

Knowledge is a mighty useful tool, to put it mildly. Even the modest electronic knowledge you have picked up from this book will enable you to service your own homemade equipment, provided you do use certain testing methods.

One of the most important methods—particularly with homemade equipment—is so obvious that it probably won't seem like a method at all. Yet it will uncover at least 80 per cent of the troubles you are apt to have with homemade gear.

Eye-and-Finger Method

Because the method is so obvious, you will probably have to make yourself do it, even though the *only* test equipment required is your eyes and fingers.

The eye-and-finger method is essentially a matter of looking things over. But even this can be done more efficiently if you know *what* to look for, and how to go about it.

Two of the most common troubles are bad soldering and errors in wiring and assembly. Of the two, bad soldering is the more common—a fact which has given kit makers nightmares for years.

Bad soldering can take a number of different forms. One is . . . .

No Connection

It is very easy, after hooking several parts to a single lug, to become distracted and forget to solder the connection.

By simply inspecting each connection carefully while tugging on the wires, you can spot bad connections. Here is where you use *both* your eyes and your fingers.

Even though you have soldered to a lug on which several wires are attached, some of them may not be connected by the solder. Again, tug on the leads while inspecting the connection.

Another type of "no connection" is one which looks all right at first glance. It even *feels* all right. But if you look it over *very* carefully, you will find that the soldering flux has, in some unexplainable way, formed a coating around the wire, insulating it from the surrounding solder. Such flux joints can be very troublesome.

In the test model of the *One Hour* radio, one of the wires running to lug E (see drawing) made a connection, but the other wire, coming to lug E from lug D, did not. We spotted the trouble by just tugging on a wire and observing the connection.

Partial Connection

The flux joint just described may result in a partial connection which "makes and breaks" or shows high resistance. There is another common type of "semi" connection — the "crystallized" joint. This one happens when the solder is heated so long that it is, in effect, burned.

You may have to find this one by observation only—the wire is usually anchored pretty securely. However, the joint will look "crystallized" that is, rough and pitted. A *good* soldered joint is always smooth and shiny. If a joint does not look this way, do it over.

When a metal lug is mounted directly on a chassis, heat is dissipated rapidly in soldering. The result may be a "cold solder" joint, the solder never becoming hot enough to make a *good* connection. The joint often *looks* rough, and it may be weak. The solution is to use the heavy tip on your iron for connections to metal lugs mounted directly on a chassis.

Another little gem is solder which flows *down* a lug, but does not fasten onto the top wire *on* the lug. Tilting the chassis while soldering will often run the solder back to where it belongs. Remember that hot solder, like water, runs downhill.

Too Many Connections

This kind of trouble is becoming more and more common as parts are made smaller and smaller. Lugs and terminals are so close together that a little solder, running around where it isn't wanted, can make an entirely unexpected connection.

Exactly this kind of trouble occurred in the test model of the utility amplifier. Excess solder flowed from insulated lug HH-1, down onto the metal **U** of the battery clip. One of the batteries shorted out, setting up some first-class trouble. However, the trouble was found by simply scrutinizing the set.

Other common spots for such trouble are on the terminal lug strips. Here, solder may run down and short to the chassis or to another lug. Still, another culprit is a phone jack, especially the miniature variety. This particular trouble showed up in the test model of the stereo amplifier chassis. A tiny sliver of solder— so tiny you could scarcely see it—shorted across two sections of the phone jack, killing the set. Careful examination located the trouble, and a quick flick with the soldering tool cured it.

Make certain the solder goes only where you want it, and no further! An unwanted connection can do as much (or more) damage than no connection, and usually is a lot harder to find.

Remember that good soldering techniques are essential in building, and that finding bad soldering is the secret for successful troubleshooting of homemade equipment. The following check chart will help you find bad solder connections.

Check Chart

☐ Visually inspect *every* connection.

☐ Tug on *every* wire to see if it makes a connection.

☐ Look for "crystallized" solder joints.

☐ Look for flux joints.

☐ See if solder has shorted from one lug to another (*including* the lugs on transistor sockets).

☐ Watch for "cold solder" joints. Use the *heavy* tip on your iron when soldering to *metal* lugs bolted to a *metal* chassis

☐ Look for places where solder has flowed from a lug or terminal to a metal *chassis*.

☐ Use only 60/40 solder—either rosin core or *radio* type— NEVER acid core.

Conscientiously following the chart will put you on the trail of at least four out of five troubles which crop up in homemade gear. Now, let's slay the smaller dragons which are left!

Wiring Errors

Next to bad soldering, the most common reason a piece of homemade gear won't "percolate" is an out-and-out error in wiring or assembling it.

Don't be embarassed when you "goof." Even experienced electronic technicians make the same mistakes—usually more than once. From this painful trial-and-error process have come the following practical techniques for reducing the trouble-finding time.

A Second Check of the Pictorial Diagram

Pictorial diagrams like the ones in this book or in any well-organized kit instructions are useful for rechecking your wiring when you suspect you have made a mistake. However, just idly comparing the diagram with the set isn't much help. Unless you force yourself to proceed step by step, you are apt to pass over the same trouble time and again—for example, hard-to-find "skipped" connection.

One method is to lay a piece of semitransparent paper (vellum is ideal) over the pictorial diagram and then, with a colored pencil, draw in each lead and part. Any mistake will become apparent because the two drawings won't match—provided, of course, you don't lose your head and draw in something that isn't there.

Another practical check is to go back through the step-by-step wiring instructions and check off each connection again. At the same time, watch for bad solder joints, or unwanted joints caused by free-flowing solder.

One of the two methods just described should pinpoint any wiring errors. A third method, also highly effective, takes a little more knowledge. To use this method, check the set against the schematic diagram. It will give you a fresh point of view—which is often all you need to spot trouble.

Parts, Too

In the relatively simple equipment described in this book, the only significant errors likely to show up are in the selection and use of parts.

For example, if you read "22K" instead of "2.2K" as the value for a resistor, and then buy and use the wrong part, finding the trouble can be a bit rough. So check each part carefully against the parts list first, and then against the schematic diagram. Be especially careful in reading the color codes—it is quite easy to misinterpret them. And don't always trust your color sense. To some people, the orange band on a resistor looks yellow!

You Haven't Found the Trouble YET?

Chances are you will have found the trouble, unless you ran into some particularly exotic one. Nevertheless, it wouldn't hurt to get acquainted with some simple but basic servicing techniques.

First, we need to look once more at the "big picture." What happens to a signal in each of the sets we "brewed up"?

Let's start with the *One Hour* radio hooked onto the headphone and speaker amplifiers. Our incoming signal is detected by the crystal diode, amplified by the transistor in the headphone amplifier, and further amplified by the transistors in the speaker amplifier.

The following block diagram will quickly illustrate what is happening in each stage.

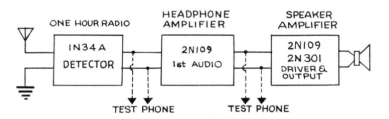

Suppose the three units, hooked together, have been working satisfactorily in the past, but now we hear nothing. Where do we start? Of course, we could aimlessly check everything. But looking for a trouble haphazardly is slow, indeed—if you find it at all.

Instead, we'll use the same method you would use on even as complicated a device as a radar set. We trace the signal through the hookup.

A signal can take many forms. In radar, for example, it is a pulse, which we can track with an oscilloscope. In our breadboard hookups, we have something simple to trace—an *audio* signal, which we can *hear* by following the signal with our crystal earphone.

An easy way to do this is to fit a small board with two sets of clips, and hook the crystal phone to one set and a pair of inexpensive test leads to the other.

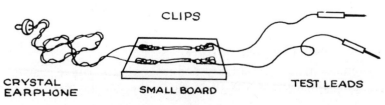

CRYSTAL
EARPHONE   SMALL BOARD   TEST LEADS

First, we apply our test leads *across* the headphone terminals of the *One Hour* radio. If it is working properly, we will hear a station. The signal may be a bit weaker than before we hooked on the amplifier (and thereby drained away some of the signal), but it should be there.

Let's assume it is. Then we *know* the first stage of our three-stage hookup is working, so we won't waste any time looking for trouble in it. Instead, we'll move on to the next stage, and put the headphone across the headphone output terminals on that amplifier.

We should hear the same signal (only louder, thanks to the amplification by the transistor). But suppose we hear nothing. For some reason, the stage is dead.

Now comes the check-out of the stage. Of course, had we just built the unit, we would start by going over the soldering, and then look for wiring errors. This time, however, we know the set did work at one time.

At this point we do a little skull work. What is most likely to change? Transistors? It's possible, but let's check something else first.

Battery? Ah yes, a battery may be run down. In fact, we just *might* have left the switch on while we were on vacation.

Having zeroed in on the most probable cause, we have two alternatives. The best one is to substitute another battery. The other is to have the battery checked, either by a friendly service technician or, as described later, with your own voltmeter.

Sure enough, the battery is dead. We replace it, and our set comes alive again.

What Have We Done?

Let's take a moment right now to see what we have just done. The method we have just used is all-important in servicing; so, if you grasp the fundamentals now, you are well on your way toward being able to troubleshoot in more complicated equipment.

1. We broke the total hookup into stages. (This was easy, since we built it in stages.)
2. We followed the signal, stage by stage, until we found the one where the signal disappeared.
3. Then we went to work on that stage and, by combining reasoning with mechanical *tests*, located the trouble.

You've Learned to Signal-Trace

Admittedly, this is an easy and somewhat idealized example. (You might make it a point to check the battery first, because it often goes bad.) Nevertheless, we have used the signal-tracing method—the backbone of almost all electronic servicing—to find the solution. Even though you probably didn't realize it at the time, you have already used the signal-tracing method while building your sets. Let's take another look at each one, starting with a block diagram of the *Easy Pocket Set.*

EASY POCKET RADIO

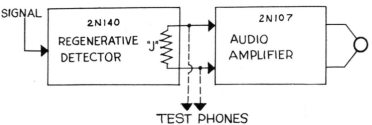

The incoming signal is detected in the first stage. To hear it, all we have to do is place our earphone across collector load resistor J and listen. Thus, we have signal-traced to the extent of determining whether the first stage is working properly. In building the set, we did this before building the amplifier stage. But we could just as well have waited until the set was completed. In fact, we might want to do so, should trouble develop later and we want to isolate it to one stage.

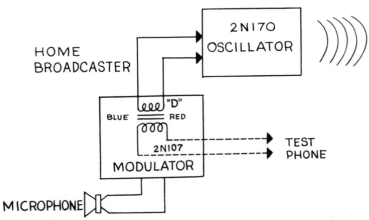

The same one-stage-at-a-time procedure was used in the home broadcaster. Testing an oscillator is a bit tricky, except with fairly complex test equipment. Fortunately, however, you can hear an oscillator in a radio tuned to the same frequency. This was the method used to check the oscillator stage in the home broadcaster.

Since the modulator is merely an audio amplifier, we can listen in with our earphone. However, there is a matter of getting a fairly high impedance, so the phone will operate. The best way to do this is to connect the phones across the primary (blue and red leads) of the transformer which couples the modulator to the oscillator. Talking into the microphone will yield a signal in the phone. Don't expect too much— the signal will be weak at best.

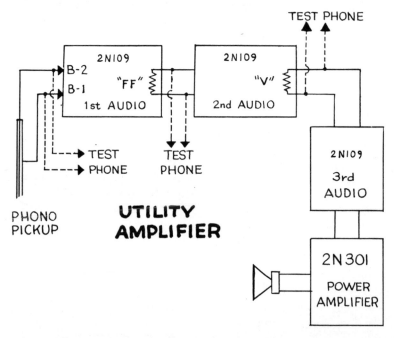

PHONO PICKUP

UTILITY AMPLIFIER

The utility amplifier actually has four stages. We can pick off the signal even before it arrives, assuming we're driving it with a high-output crystal phono cartridge. Such a cartridge will generate sufficient signal to be heard with a crystal earphone. Simply connect the earphone across the proper terminals underneath the record player, or hook the phone between the "hot" (insulated) phono input plug and the metal chassis.

This hookup is ideal for testing the phono cartridge. Therefore, we start signal-tracing right where the signal should begin—at the cartridge.

Moving along, we can pick the signal off across collector load resistor FF in the first transistor stage. Since this stage is primarily for impedance matching, there is actually a signal loss across it. Hence, you will hear a somewhat weaker signal than you will from the crystal pickup.

At the output of the next stage, we'll hear a pretty decent signal, since now we have one transistor doing some honest-to-goodness amplifying. This signal appears across resistor V.

Because we must match the low-impedance input of the power transistor, there is no convenient high-impedance point for our earphone and, therefore, no easy way to check the third stage. However, if the signal goes into it, but nothing comes out of the speaker, the trouble must be in the final two stages. Since they contain relatively few parts, troubleshooting from there on is not too difficult. Besides, we have accomplished the purpose of signal-tracing—to narrow the troubleshooting area to where we can handle it, using other techniques which will be discussed later.

Checking Short Wave Set

The test procedure for this set is well-covered in Chapter 11. In our initial check of the short wave receiver, we put a signal from the *One Hour* Radio into the base of the first audio stage before adding the detector stage. In may ways the little radio is hard to beat for this purpose, because it generates a wide band of frequencies in the form of music and voice.

You may want to purchase a small signal injector which will put out a highly-useful single-tone signal for injection into RF, audio, and TV circuits. Many imported units can be purchased for about $4.00.

Testing Stereo Amplifier

As an example, the signal injector is ideal for checking the driver stage of your stereo amplifier. Apply the signal to test point C1. Once the amplifier is completed, the injector can be used to test the module at point L-5 in Chapter 13. The output at this point will be lower than at point C-1 because we are bypassing the driver stage.

In Quick Summary

The signal-tracing techniques outlined should enable you to pinpoint trouble to one—or at most, two—stages in any equipment you have built so far. Usually this will solve your service problem because, working with new parts and transistors, it is highly unlikely you will be the victim of bad parts. The next step is to check over very carefully both the soldered connections and the wiring in the stage where the trouble is apparent. Such a check should locate the trouble.

If not, we have one more string for our bow! With a low-cost test instrument, we can check the parts—good experience although, as we said, bad parts are probably not the cause of your troubles. The only exception would be parts burned by careless soldering, or transistors damaged because a wiring error applied voltage to the wrong elements.

Your First Test Instrument

Just as in buying hi-fi gear, it is better to take it easy when buying test equipment—at least, until you know your way around. An experienced technician can do an amazing amount of servicing with no equipment at all—just by observing and reasoning. Thus, there is no point, when starting out, in saddling yourself with test gear that can be even more puzzling than the units you are testing.

For your first effort, you may want to buy a low-cost, 1,000-ohms-per-volt multimeter. Also called a multimeter, volt-ohm-

meter, or a pocket tester, it will provide a fair indication of AC and DC voltages, plus DC current and resistance.

Electronic technicians prefer an instrument with a sensitivity of 20,000 ohms per volt or better, and for a good reason—they do not load circuits as much. However, they are a little more expensive.

Using the Ohmmeter Section

The ohmmeter section is a good one to start with, since it is rather difficult to do anything wrong here!

Your meter will have two test leads, one red and one black. Assuming the meter has pin jacks instead of a switch (the latter, although convenient, is much more confusing), put the black lead in the "DC" common jack (see the meter instructions) and the red lead in the "ohms" jack.

Now, short the leads together. The needle will move all the way across the scale, indicating *no* resistance. If it stops partway, turn the zero adjustment on the meter until the needle is on zero.

Measuring Resistors

Connect a resistor within the range of the meter (for example, a 10,000-ohm resistor) to the two test leads. The meter should read 10,000 ohms. (It will probably take a bit of doing to decipher this reading, but it is there.)

That is all to measuring resistors, except for one more item. When the resistor is in a set, disconnect one end from the circuit by unsoldering the lead or clipping it with your diagonals. Some other part in the set may be in parallel with the resistor. If so, the reading will be inaccurate. This clipping-before-measuring is standard in servicing. That is what we meant earlier when we called diagonals a "test" instrument.

Checking Capacitors

Our simple meter is scarcely the last word in instruments for checking capacitors, although it will show up shorted ones. To check, connect the meter as for measuring resistance, and apply its leads to *both* capacitor leads.

If it is a mica, ceramic, or paper capacitor, you should get no reading. If it is a small electrolytic of the type used in transistor equipment, the needle will flick (as the capacitor charges) and then climb to the high end of the scale, indicating a very high resistance. If not, the capacitor probably is bad. One precaution—observe the capacitor polarity by running the *black* meter lead to the *negative,* and the *red* lead to the *positive,* capacitor lead.

Checking for Connections

One of the most useful features of an ohmmeter is its ability to easily reveal *no* resistance—in other words, no connection.

Many times, you can use this feature to ward off trouble from an unwanted connection. For example, the antenna variable capacitor, when mounted in its plastic "sandwich" on the end of the short-wave chassis, must not slide around and possibly short to the chassis.

Simply touching one ohmmeter test lead to the shaft and the other to the chassis will reveal whether there *is* a connection or not.

Similarly, you can check soldered connections when an open one is suspected—for example, between *every* wire and the lug it is hooked to (this includes every lead where more than one goes to the same lug).

Coils and Transformers

Most coil troubles stem from their being open. To check, simply apply the test leads to both ends of the coil and then, if there is a tap, from it to either end. The same procedure is useful for checking transformer windings. With high-priced ohmmeters you can measure the actual DC resistance of coil and transformer windings. However, our low-cost unit ordinarily will not show *any* resistance in the winding, but a straight-through connection instead.

Voltage Checks

When working with low voltages and a relatively insensitive meter, voltage checks within the set won't mean much. However, a 0-15 volt DC range will allow us to check 9-volt batteries or 1½-volt cells. Actually, however, the best way to test the battery is in the set and with the set on. If the battery is more than 10 per cent low, you have a right to be suspicious; if more than 20, it is probably bad. The only definite check, though, is to substitute another battery.

Checking Diodes

Although not foolproof, the following check usually will spot bad diodes. First, hook the leads to the diode, and note the reading. Then reverse the leads, and again note the reading. If the diodes are all right, there should be a *marked* difference between the readings—one will be quite high (for example 50,000 ohms), and the other quite low (for example, 1,000 ohms). Unless there is a *considerable* difference, however, the diode probably is bad.

Checking Transistors

The best check for a transistor is substitution. However, we can use our ohmmeter to roughly check the small audio transistors (but *not* the larger power transistor used for the final speaker stage of the utility amplifier).

For our check, we'll use the ohmmeter portion of the meter (0-100,000 ohm scale). First, fit a 3-terminal transistor socket with leads hooked to three Fahnestock clips on a board, and plug the transistor into the socket. Hook the meter to the clips coming from the base and the collector, and note the reading. Now *reverse* the leads and again note the reading. One should be much higher; this is the one we want for our next step. So, hook the leads in whichever way gives the *higher* reading.

With the leads so connected, short the emitter clip to the base clip. The resistance reading should fall. Leave the one test lead connected to the collector clip, but remove the one to the base clip and hook it to the emitter clip. Note the reading. Now short the emitter clip to the base clip. The resistance should rise. If you get this increase, plus the decrease mentioned before, the transistor is probably all right.

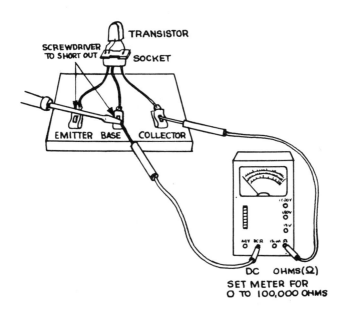

TRANSISTOR
SCREWDRIVER TO SHORT OUT
SOCKET
EMITTER BASE COLLECTOR

DC   OHMS(Ω)
SET METER FOR
O TO 100,000 OHMS

If the transistor is bad, it will act *quite* differently from this. Exactly *how* is difficult to predict. The important point is that it will.

This test will weed out bad transistors. It will not find those which are simply weak or "leaky"—a less common trouble, fortunately.

Finally

You can do a lot more with your volt-ohmmeter. The uses mentioned will help you get acquainted with your instrument. Now, one more point.

In troubleshooting *any* electronic equipment, first look it over thoroughly. If you built it yourself, examine the wiring and *every* soldered connection systematically. Pay special attention to the soldering. A poor soldering job is the number-one troublemaker in homemade gear.

If you still have trouble, isolate the defect to one stage by signal-tracing. Again look for wiring mistakes or bad soldering. Finally, check the individual parts with a volt-ohmmeter using the techniques outlined in this chapter. (This final step is rarely necessary in home-built gear made from new parts.)

Where Do We Go From Here?

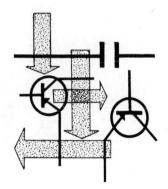

If you have built all or most of the sets in this book, and if you have thoroughly digested the chapters on parts, symbols, reading diagrams, hi-fi, and servicing, you have made an excellent start in the exciting world of electronics. Most important of all, you have had an opportunity to sample quite a variety of electronic activities.

Now, you're probably asking yourself: "Where do I go from here?"

Where *do* you go from here? Perhaps your kibitzing on the radio amateur bands has fired up your interest in becoming a ham. If so, fine! You now have all or most of the basic electronic theory you will need to qualify for your novice license. For you, it's just a short step toward your own ham radio station.

Or maybe your earlier venture into hi-fi has convinced you that you won't rest until you can play a recording of a harpsichord and have it sound like the real thing. Moreover, you have one big advantage over many hi-fi enthusiasts: you can troubleshoot and service your own hi-fi rig. (For more information on servicing, the author's book *Introduction to Electronic Servicing for the Beginner* is recommended.)

Every person dreams of making his life's work what he enjoys doing the most. Perhaps servicing electronic equipment is so interesting that you would like to make it your career; or maybe you just want to do part-time servicing to supplement your income. There are good trade schools and correspondence courses. But don't stop there. Electronics is growing so rapidly that you have to be an avid reader to keep up with the developments.

There is a new and almost unknown profession that will appeal to those of you who have a flair for writing. This is technical writing and editing. Not too long ago, all technical books and manuals were written by engineers and other technical personnel. But as equipment became more and more complex, literally bales of operating manuals were needed. Soon, these people were so swamped with paperwork that they didn't have time to do their regular jobs. Out of this dilemma evolved the technical writer or editor, who was a cross between a writer and an engineer. This hybrid character was either an engineer with an aptitude for writing, or a writer with technical training. His job was and is to boil down the mass of technical information into a readable and understanding book, manual, or magazine article. So, if you, too, like to write and, at the same time, also want to put your technical training to work, you might seriously consider becoming a technical writer or editor.

Learn—But Have Fun, Too!

It is true that, to stay on top in the mushrooming electronics field, you must read constantly. However, this won't be a chore. On the contrary, you will enjoy it because you will have a ringside seat in the world of tomorrow.

In any event, whether you are cultivating a money-making hobby or searching for a career, or whether you just need the therapy of working with your hands to get rid of tension, you'll find tremendous pleasure in electronics. And you will agree with the writer, who will end this book on the same note it began:

Electronics is just plain fun . . Enjoy yourself!

Appendix

Substituting Transistors

Electronics is such a rapidly-changing art that new products are introduced constantly. This is especially true for transistors. In addition, manufacturers frequently stop production on a given type of transistor, particularly when it has been replaced by an improved version.

Most of the transistors specified for units in this book are of a noncritical nature; similar types may be substituted for any of the transistors specified. Of course, the builder should *try* to use the ones specified. This is the best way to insure good results from the equipment. *If* the specified type is not available locally or from one of the large mail-order parts suppliers, the next step is to choose a substitute, following the data included below:

2N109   Description: PNP general purpose audio transistor. Other similar types: CK-722, 2N217, 2N270, 2N415, 2N466, 2N1305, 2N1348, GE-2, SK3004, ECG102, HEP-254, DS-26, TR-05, AA-1, AT-30H.

2N140   Description: PNP oscillator - converter transistor. Other similar types: CK-768, 2N219, 2N1280, 2N1316, GE-1, SK3005, ECG-100, HEP3, DS-25, TR-14, AA-1, HF12H.

2N170   Description: NPN general purpose RF-AF transistor. Other similar types: 2N164, 2N634, 2N1995, GE-5, SK-3011, ECG-101, DS-75, TR-08, AA-2, NR5.

2N301   Description: PNP medium power audio transistor. Other similar types: 2N376, 2N1227, 2N1359, 2N1534, 2N1544A, GE-3, SK3009, ECG104, HEP230, DS-503, PT40, AA4.

Lead Identification

In making substitutions, it is extremely important that the *leads* of the transistors are properly identified. This means you must carefully determine which are the "base," "collector," and "emitter," leads. Normally, it is not difficult to do, since there should be a diagram packed with the transistor.